## TABLE OF CONTENTS

Welcome to the world of Infocom.

Close to fifteen years ago, Zork made its first appearance on the campus of MIT. Inspired by the first text adventure, "Advent" and such role playing games as "Dungeons & Dragons," Zork was the first game to use an interpretive English parser that understood whole sentences rather than two-word commands. The game was so popular that it was translated to almost every computer platform conceivable, and Infocom was born.

Great games like Zork and the Enchanter series have not been in stores for years now, but the public still remembers them. With video games being such a new thing, it's hard to conceive of video game nostalgia. But somehow, Infocom has managed to establish this category. Users still call our offices asking where they can find copies of such games as "Hitchhiker's Guide" or "The Lurking Horror."

Infocom made classic games. The heart and soul of Infocom games was imagination, not only on the author's part, but also on the player's part. Reading the text of an Infocom adventure is like reading a good novel. Since these games are text based, they can be enjoyed on most machines, not just the latest whiz-bang systems with the hottest CPUs and graphics cards. The "graphics" in these products never become obsolete.

So, I hope you have as much fun playing and re-playing these "lost" adventures as I have had over the past 10 years. They are something special that should be shared with younger gamers who have never seen a text adventure. They are a piece of video game history.

Kevin Cheung

Kevin Cheung
Lost Treasures Re-mastering Engineer

Credits :
Shell programming & Re-mastering : Kevin Cheung
Manual & Hint book Re-mastering : Kelly Zmak and Pat Zmak
Software QA: Kelly Rodgers & Mike Coustier

**Communicating with Interactive Fiction** ( If you are not familiar with Infocom's Interactive Fiction, please read this section.)

With Interactive Fiction, you type your commands in plain English each time you see the prompt (>). Most of the sentences that The STORIES will understand are imperative sentences. See the examples below.

When you have finished typing your input, press the RETURN (or ENTER) key. The STORY will then respond, telling you whether your request is possible at this point in the story, and what happened as a result.

The STORY recognizes your words by their first six letters, and all subsequent letters are ignored. Therefore, CANDLE, CANDLEs, and CANDLEstick would all be treated as the same word.

To move around, just type the direction you want to go. Directions can be abbreviated: NORTH to N, SOUTH to S, EAST to E, WEST .to W, NORTHEAST to NE, NORTHWEST to NW, SOUTHEAST to SE, SOUTHWEST to SW, UP to U, and DOWN to D IN and OUT will also work in certain places.

There are many different kinds of sentences used in "LOST TREASURES". Here are some examples:

>WALK TO THE NORTH
>WEST
>NE
>DOWN
>TAKE THE BIRDCAGE
>OPEN THE PANEL
>READ ABOUT DIMWIT FLATHEAD
>LOOK UP MEGABOZ IN THE ENCYCLOPEDIA
>LIE DOWN IN THE PINK SOFA
>EXAMINE THE SHINY COIN
>PUT THE RUSTY KEY IN THE CARDBOARD BOX
>SHOW MY BOW TIE TO THE BOUNCER
>HIT THE CRAWLING CRAB WITH THE GIANT NUTCRACKER
>ASK THE COWARDLY KING ABOUT THE CROWN JEWELS

You can use multiple objects with certain verbs if you separate them by the word AND or by a comma. Some examples:

>TAKE THE BOOK AND THE FROG
>DROP THE JAR OF PEANUT BUTTER, THE SPOON, AND THE LEMMING FOOD
>PUT THE EGG AND THE PENCIL IN THE CABINET

You can include several inputs on one line if you separate them by the word THEN or by a period. Each input will handled in order, as though you had typed them individually at separate prompts. For example, you could type all of the following at once, before pressing the RETURN (or ENTER) key:
>TURN ON THE LIGHT. TAKE THE BOOK THEN READ ABOUT THE JESTER IN THE BOOK

If The STORY doesn't understand one of the sentences on your input line, or if an unusual event occurs, it will ignore the rest of your input line.

The words IT and ALL can be very useful. For example:
>EXAMINE THE APPLE. TAKE IT. EAT IT
>CLOSE THE HEAVY METAL DOOR. LOCK IT
>PICK UP THE GREEN BOOT. SMELL IT. PUT IT ON.
>TAKE ALL
>TAKE ALL THE TOOLS
>DROP ALL THE TOOLS EXCEPT THE WRENCH AND THE MINIATURE HAMMER
>TAKE ALL FROM THE CARTON
>GIVE ALL BUT THE RUBY SLIPPERS TO THE WICKED WITCH

The word ALL refers to every visible object except those inside something else. If there were an apple on the ground and an orange inside a cabinet, TAKE ALL would take the apple but not the orange.

There are three kinds of questions that you can ask: WHERE IS (something), WHAT IS (something), and WHO IS (someone). For example:
>WHO IS LORD DIMWIT?
>WHAT IS A GRUE?
>WHERE IS EVERYBODY?

When you meet intelligent creatures, you can talk to them by typing their name, then a comma, then whatever you want to say to them. Here are some examples:
>JESTER, HELLO
>GUSTAR WOOMAX, TELL ME ABOUT THE COCONUT
>UNCLE OTTO, GIVE ME YOUR WALLET
>HORSE, WHERE IS YOUR SADDLE?
>BOY, RUN HOME THEN CALL THE POLICE
>MIGHTY WIZARD, TAKE THIS POISONED APPLE. EAT IT

Notice that in the last two examples, you are giving the character more than one command on the same input line. Keep in mind, however, that many creatures don't care for idle chatter; your actions will speak louder than your words.

**Infocom Basic Commands ( Please read this section before playing The Lost Treasures. )**

BRIEF - This command fully describe a location only the first time you enter it. On subsequent visits, only the name of the location and any objects present will be described. The adventures will begin in BRIEF mode, and remain in BRIEF mode unless you use the VERBOSE or SUPERBRIEF commands
SUPERBRIEF displays only the name of a place you have entered, even if you have never been there before. In this mode, not even mention objects are described. Of course, you can always get a full description of your location and the items there by typing LOOK. In SUPERBRIEF mode, the blank line between turns will be eliminated. This mode is meant for players who are already familiar with the geography.
The VERBOSE command gives a complete description of each location, and the objects in it, every time you enter a location, even if you've been there before.

DIAGNOSE - This will give you a report of your physical condition.

INVENTORY - This will give you a list what you are carrying and wearing. You can abbreviate INVENTORY to I.

LOOK - This will give you a full description of your location. You can abbreviate LOOK to L.

QUIT - This lets you stop. If you want to save your position before quitting, you must use the SAVE command.

RESTORE - This restores a previously saved position.

RESTART - This stops the story and starts it over from the beginning.

SAVE - This saves a “snapshot” of your current position. You can return to a saved position in the future using the RESTORE command.

SCRIPT - This command tells your printer to begin making a transcript of the story. A transcript may aid your memory, but is not necessary.

Infocom Basic Commands (cont.)

SCORE- This command will show your current score and a ranking which is based on that score.

SUPERBRIEF - This command gives you the sparest level of description See BRIEF above.

TIME - This command gives you the current time in the story. ( Not available in all games)

UNSCRIPT - This tells your printer to stop making a transcript.

VERBOSE - This command gives you the wordiest level of description. See BRIEF above.

VERSION - Shows you the release number and the serial number of your copy of the story.

WAIT - Causes time in the story to pass. Since nothing happens until you type a sentence and press RETURN (or ENTER), you could leave your computer, take a nap, then return to the story to find that nothing has changed. You can use WAIT to make time pass in the story without doing anything. For example, if you met a wizard, you might WAIT to see if he will say anything; if you were aboard a flying carpet, you might WAIT to see where it goes.

**Be sure to read the "Special Commands" section in selected games.**

# Zork:

# The Great Underground Empire

Welcome to Zork!
You are about to experience a classic interactive fantasy, set in a magical universe. The Zork Trilogy is set in the ruins of an ancient empire lying far underground. You, a dauntless treasure-hunter, are venturing into this dangerous land in search of wealth and adventure. Because each part of the Zork saga is a completely independent story, you can play them in any order. However, because Zork I is the least difficult, it is usually the best place to begin. Many strange tales have been told of the fabulous treasure, exotic creatures, and diabolical puzzles in the Great Underground Empire. As an aspiring adventurer, you will undoubtedly want to locate these treasures and deposit them in your trophy case. You'd better equip yourself with a source of light (for the caverns are dark) and weapons (for some of the inhabitants are unfriendly - especially the thief, a skilled pickpocket and ruthless opponent).

About the Authors
Dave Lebling was born in Washington, D. C., in a hospital that was torn down soon thereafter. He grew up in suburban Maryland. He attended the Massachusetts Institute of Technology, and worked at M.I.T.'s Laboratory for Computer Science, where he developed an interest in computer entertainments. He co-authored the original mainframe Zork. He co-authored Zork I, Zork II, Zork III, and Enchanter, and wrote Starcross, Suspect, Spellbreaker, and The Lurking Horror on his own. His long-range ambition is to have a library with room enough for all his books to be taken out of storage. His short range ambition is to keep the squirrels out of his birdseed. Marc Blank, a graduate of the Massachusetts Institute of Technology and the Albert Einstein College of Medicine, is one of the original founders of Infocom. He co-authored the original mainframe version of Zork at M.I.T., and went on to become one of the pioneers in the field of interactive fiction. At Infocom, he co-authored The Zork Trilogy and Enchanter, and was sole author of Deadline, the first interactive mystery. Marc also wrote Border Zone, Infocom's first tale of intrigue.

CHAPTER ONE

# The Bellicose King

In 659 GUE*, the Kingdom of Quendor was relatively small, encompassing seven-and-a-half provinces on the western shore of the Great Sea, an agrarian land whose major products were rope and mosquito netting. It was the thirty-first year of the reign of Zilbo III, part of a dynasty dating back more than six centuries to Entharion the Wise, the first King of Quendor. However, that dynasty was about to end with the ascension of Duncanthrax to the throne of Quendor on the final day of 659.

Little is known about what became of Zilbo after 659. Some say he was killed during a palace revolt, or simply died from too much reveling while celebrating the upcoming New Year. There is evidence that he was exiled to a villa where he invented the card game Double Fanucci.

Likewise, historians disagree about Duncanthrax's life prior to 659. A petition signed by palace guards in 657, asking for an increase in the mosquito netting allotment, bears a signature that looks suspiciously like "Duncanthrax." Some historians insist that Duncanthrax was general of the Royal Militia. One legend even suggests that Duncanthrax was a demon who assumed human form. Another legend describes him as a former rope salesman.

Whatever his origins, Duncanthrax quickly developed a reputation for cruelty, bloodthirstiness and aggressiveness, thus earning himself the nickname "The Bellicose King." He raised a tremendous army and began a systematic conquest of the neighboring kingdoms. Within three years, Duncanthrax ruled an empire that controlled virtually all the land between the Great Sea and the Kovalli Desert.

*Adding "GUE" after a year did not become common practice until the latter part of the eighth century.

CHAPTER TWO

# An Empire Goes Underground

In 665, the forces of Duncanthrax vanquished the Antharian Armada at the famous battle of Fort Griffspotter. The island-nation of Antharia was, at the time, the world's premier sea power, and this victory gave Duncanthrax undisputed control of the Great Sea and put the superb ship-building facilities of Antharia at his disposal. (The conquest of Antharia also gave Duncanthrax possession of Antharia's famed granola mines. Unfortunately, no one in Quendor liked granola.)

Within months, Quendor's navy was returning from voyages with tales of a magical land on the distant eastern shore of the Great Sea. Duncanthrax was incensed that this vast land existed outside his dominion, and spent many nights storming the halls of his castle bellowing at his servants and advisors. Then, one day, he had a sudden inspiration: assemble a huge fleet, cross the Great Sea and conquer the lands on the eastern shore. Not only would he extend his empire, but he'd finally have a market for all that useless granola.

As Duncanthrax's invasion swept across the new lands, he made a startling discovery: huge caverns and tunnels, populated by gnomes, trolls and other magical races, all of whom loved granola. Even as Duncanthrax conquered this region, his imagination was inspired by this natural underground formation.

If these caverns and tunnels were possible in nature, so might they be formed by humans! Duncanthrax realized that by burrowing into the ground he could increase the size of his empire fivefold or even tenfold!

The Frobozz Magic Construction Company (the forerunner of the modern industrial giant FrobozzCo International) was formed to undertake this project in 668. For the remaining 20 years of Duncanthrax's reign, cavern-building continued at a breakneck pace. The natural caverns in the eastern lands were expanded tremendously, and new caverns and passages were dug in the western lands, chiefly in the vicinity of Duncanthrax's castle, Egreth. By the time of his death in 688, Duncanthrax ruled virtually all territory in the known world, above and below ground.

## EXPENDITURES OF THREE ROYAL GOVERNMENTS

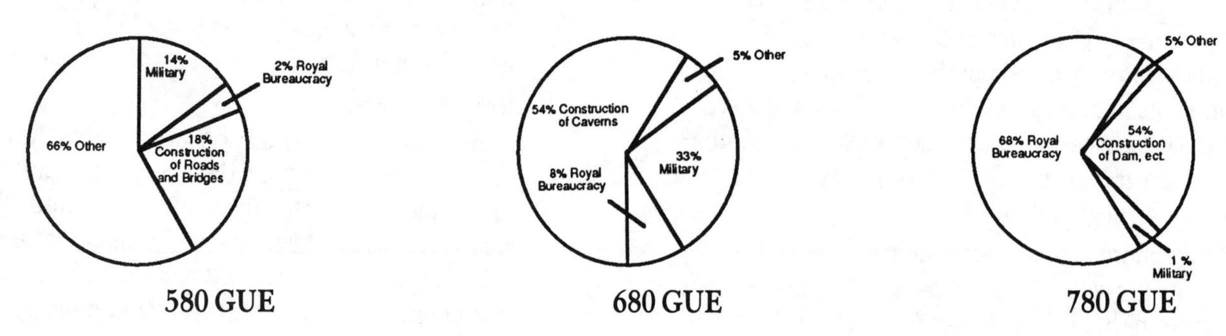


These pie charts show the fiscal priorities of the Empire under three kings who ruled centuries apart: Bozbo IV, Duncanthrax and Dimwit Flathead.

CHAPTER THREE

# The Flatheads

After Duncanthrax, the throne was occupied by a long series of his descendants. These were unspectacular rulers, who took on the surname Flathead, for obscure reasons not necessarily related to the planar shape of their pates. During this period, there was very little change in the Empire, as the conquered kingdoms were assimilated into Quendor and the frantic pace of tunneling gradually abated.

In 770, nearly a century after the death of Duncanthrax, his great-great-grandson, Dimwit Flathead, assumed the throne. Lord Dimwit, as he liked to be called, was a colorful character, but was also the single worst ruler the Empire ever produced. His vanity was surpassed only by his outrageous sense of proportion. For example, his coronation took 13 years to plan (and therefore took place two-thirds of the way through his reign), lasted an additional year and a half, and cost 12 times the Empire's GNP.

Dimwit was the first king to call Quendor "The Great Underground Empire," and within a few years the new name had completely displaced the older one. Dimwit also renamed the Great Sea "the Flathead Ocean," and seemed to prefer the newer lands on the eastern shore. He even moved the Empire's capital from Egreth (in the westlands) to Flatheadia (in the eastlands).

While Dimwit certainly inherited Duncanthrax's ambition and ingratiating personality, he directed them in a somewhat less productive fashion. Whereas Duncanthrax used his power to expand his empire, Dimwit was motivated to realize his bizarre whims. Raising the kingdom's tax rate to just over 98%, Dimwit began a series of grandiose projects that soon earned him the title "Flathead the Excessive." Among these projects: the construction of mammoth Flood Control Dam Number Three (a massive edifice with virtually no useful purpose, since it never rains underground), the creation of the Royal Museum (to house the crown jewels), the defoliation of four hundred thousand acres of lush forest (to erect a nine-bloit-high statue of himself in the Fublio Valley) and the production of the enormous granola smelters of Plumbat.

Just before his death in 789, Flathead was rumored to be planning his greatest dream: the creation of a new continent in the center of the Flathead Ocean. The outline and contours of the new continent would have been a gigantic reproduction of his own visage.

## IMPORTANT POLITICAL AND CULTURAL EVENTS

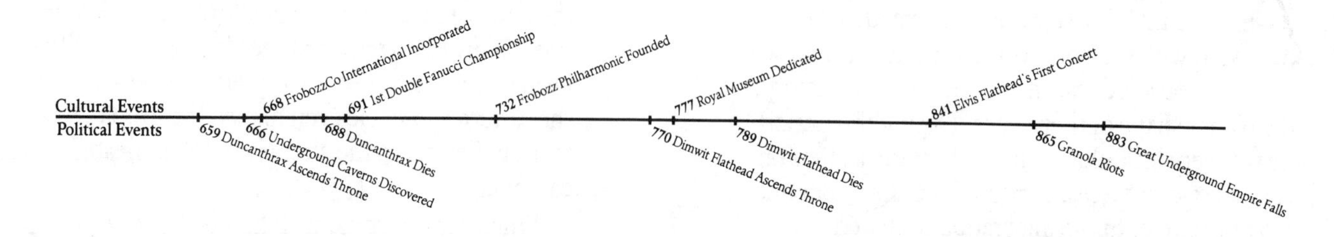


This time line shows the dates of some of the events that shaped the history of The Great Underground Empire. Cultural events are listed above the time line and political events are listed below.

### Questions, Discussions, Projects and Further Readings:

1. How many things can you think of that are named after the Flatheads? Make a list.
2. Try to collect 10 zorkmids from everyone on your block, telling them that the money will be used to erect a giant statue of yourself. Use force if necessary. See if the others on your block begin to resent you.
3. Read *The Lives of the Twelve Flatheads*, by Boswell Barwell.

CHAPTER FOUR

# Fall of the Empire

Although Dimwit was certainly the most flagrantly indulgent ruler in the history of The Great Underground Empire, most of the Flatheads who followed him did their best to uphold the tradition of excessiveness. The high level of taxation continued, although the money was increasingly spent not on massive construction projects but on extravagant parties and long vacation trips for members of the Royal Family.

In 883, after countless years of decadence and overtaxation, The Great Underground Empire collapsed, the Royal Treasury was sacked and everyone moved somewhere else.

## THE KINGS OF QUENDOR

| The Entharion Dynasty | |
|---|---|
| Entharion the Wise | 0–41 |
| Mysterion the Brave | 41–55 |
| Zylon the Aged | 55–398 |
| Zilbo I | 398–423 |
| Bozbo I | 423–429 |
| Zilbo II | 429–451 |
| Harmonious Fzort | 451–477 |
| Bozbo II | 477–481 |
| Thaddium Fzort | 481–545 |
| Mumbo I | 545–569 |
| Bozbo III | 569–575 |
| Bozbo IV | 575–619 |
| Mumbo II | 619–628 |
| Zilbo III | 628–659 |

| The Flathead Dynasty | |
|---|---|
| Duncanthrax the Bellicose | 659–688 |
| Belwit the Flat | 688–701 |
| Frobwit the Flatter | 701–727 |
| Timberthrax Flathead | 727–738 |
| Phloid Flathead | 738–755 |
| Mumberthrax Flathead | 755–770 |
| Dimwit Flathead | 770–789 |
| Loowit Flathead | 789–813 |
| Duncwit Flathead | 813–843 |
| Barbawit Flathead | 843–845 |
| Idwit Oogle Flathead | 845–881 |
| Wurb Flathead | 881–883 |

This table shows the rulers of Quendor, later known as The Great Underground Empire, through its collapse in 883 GUE.

# Zork II:
## The Wizard of Frobozz

Welcome to Zork!
You are about to experience a classic interactive fantasy, set in a magical universe. The ZORK Trilogy is set in the ruins of an ancient empire lying far underground. You, a dauntless treasure-hunter, are venturing into this dangerous land in search of wealth and adventure Because each part of the ZORK saga is a completely independent story, you can play the any order. In Zork II, you will explore a long-hidden region of the Empire, a region dominated by the Wizard of Frobozz. The Wizard was once a respected Enchanter, but when his powers began to fade he was exiled by Lord Dimwit Flathead the Excessive. Now bordering on senility, the Wizard is still a force to be reckoned with. Your goal, as you venture into the Wizard's realm, is to avoid his capricious tricks and learn to control his magical powers.

# ANTHARIA

**LOCAL GOVERNMENT:** Antharia is ruled by a council of four "Elders"—one from the Shipbuilding Guild, one from the Granola Miners Guild, one from the Marble Cutters Guild, and one from a popular waterfront pub called "Emu's."

**WEATHER:** Except for an occasional hurricane in late summer, Antharian weather is picture-perfect. Leave your umbrella home, but don't forget to pack your swim suit and scuba gear!

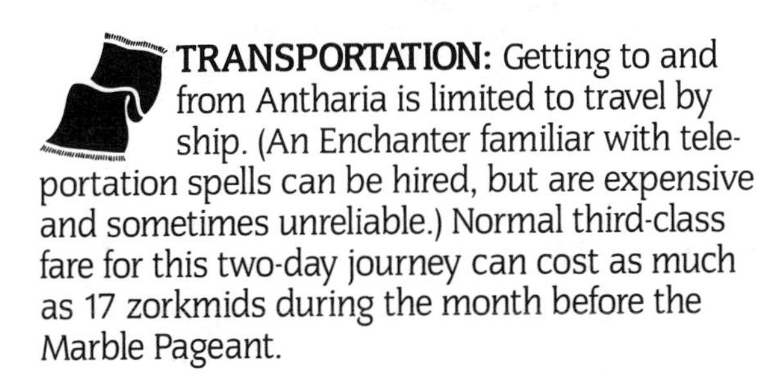

**TRANSPORTATION:** Getting to and from Antharia is limited to travel by ship. (An Enchanter familiar with teleportation spells can be hired, but are expensive and sometimes unreliable.) Normal third-class fare for this two-day journey can cost as much as 17 zorkmids during the month before the Marble Pageant.

**LODGING:** The world-famous Zilton Hotel in downtown Anthar features plush accommodations and easy access to most of the island's sights. Prices range from 6 to 24 zorkmids per night. More economical lodgings can be found at the bucolic Pterodactyl Inn. Every room features a stunning view of the cliffs overlooking the lovely north shore of the island, and rates range from 2 to 8 zorkmids per night.

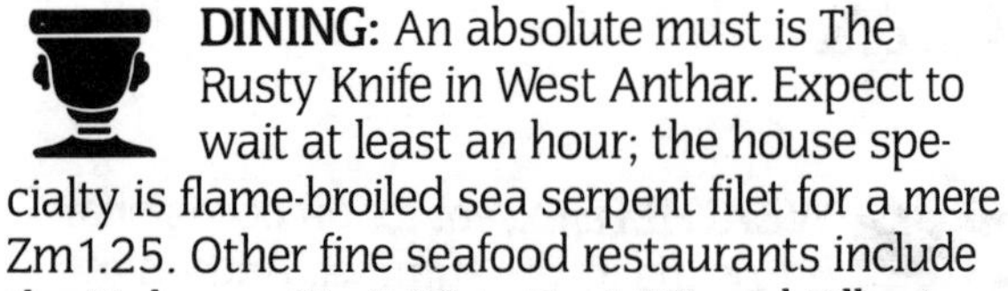

**DINING:** An absolute must is The Rusty Knife in West Anthar. Expect to wait at least an hour; the house specialty is flame-broiled sea serpent filet for a mere Zm1.25. Other fine seafood restaurants include the Finhouse (Zm0.50 to Zm1.50) and Zilbar's (Zm0.35 to Zm1.50).

**THINGS TO SEE:** The shipbuilding factories of South Anthar are an amazing sight; plan to spend at least half a day. Tours for 1 zorkmid are available every hour from dawn until dusk. The burgeoning marble industry offers many exciting sights: the gaping mines in the Peltoid Valley, the cutting and polishing guilds at work, the 20-bloit conveyor belt at the port of Marba. Despite the reduced output since the Granola Riots, the granola mines in the north make an interesting visit if you can stand the smell. No trip to the island would be complete without a cruise on the island's only glass-bottom boat, the Bella Quease. The cruise leaves an hour before noon, and costs Zm2.25 (children under 12, Zm1.50).

**SEASONAL EVENTS:** The Marble Pageant, held annually in mid-spring, is highly recommended. However, during the month of the Pageant, hotel space becomes scarce, and many prices are inflated. Shark-wrestling, held every weekend during the summer at Anthar's Flathead Stadium, is an exciting experience if you can stomach the gore. Admission is Zm0.75.

**FACTS:**
**Land Area:** 959 square bloits
**Capital:** Anthar
**Nickname:** The Island Province
**Flower:** The Spenseweed
**Motto:** "Hieya wizka" ("Hello sailor")

# GREATER BORPHEE

**LOCAL GOVERNMENT:** Greater Borphee is administered by a staff of part-time volunteer managers, whose decisions are ratified at least three times per year, but not more than every other week, by a series of local forums.

**TRANSPORTATION:** Borphee is probably the single most accessible vacation spot in the Empire. From anywhere in the Borphee River valley, travel by ferry is easy and inexpensive. If you wish to travel by sea, Borphee has an excellent, busy harbor. By land, the Coast Road connects Borphee with the ancient cities to the north as well as the populous southlands.

**WEATHER:** Thanks to the nearby ocean, Borphee has a very moderate climate. The rainy season lasts most of the winter, and summers tend to be humid.

**LODGING:** Motel Spell is a highly commercialized tourist trap with overdone touches such as the issuing of self-casting REZROV spells instead of keys. Rooms start at 5 zorkmids. Be forewarned, patrons who miss check-out time will have their families turned into newts and their luggage turned into bat guano. The Borphee Inn, run by the Frobozz Magic Hotel Company, is comfortable and surprisingly affordable. While penthouse suites can run upwards of 33 zorkmids per day, basement rooms are available for as little as 3 zorkmids (but make your reservations well in advance).

**DINING:** The Potion Palace, at the Borphee Inn, features a delightful menu of enchanted dishes. Waiters are a thing of the past at the Palace, as your mind is probed to discover the perfect meal for your taste, which then poofs into existence right at your table. A nightly floor show features dancing nymphs; expect to spend at least Zm4. Also highly recommended is the Smokestack, where even the heartiest of meals costs under a zorkmid.

**THINGS TO SEE:** Borphee is the Kingdom's fastest-growing industrial city, with the magic scroll and potion factories leading the way. Both Spellbound and United Thaumaturgy offer free tours of their facilities. (Spellbound's deluxe tour costs Zm3, but it includes casting a time travel spell that gives you three extra hours in your schedule.) G.U.E. Tech, the newest of the Moss-League Colleges, produces the young Enchanters of tomorrow. Many graduates have gone on to start their own magic companies, and have become an identifiable subculture known as "Yuppies," or "Young Underground Professionals."

Just a short trip south of the city are some of the most beautiful stretches of beach anywhere on the Flathead Ocean, including the very dunes where "Beach Blanket Fanucci" was filmed. Borphee nightlife is renowned throughout the Empire; Studio Frob on the wharf features an excellent Phlog and Tonic for Zm0.25. Warning: the Borphee Observation Tower is a complete waste of money. Admittance is Zm7, and the air in downtown Borphee never provides visibility of more than a fraction of a bloit.

**SEASONAL EVENTS:** Borphee is the site of the annual Double Fanucci Championships. During the first week in autumn, the entire province fills up with every Double Fanucci fanatic in the kingdom. Tickets to each game in the finals cost 3 zorkmids, but usually sell out within hours. Scalpers command as much as 20 zorkmids for a good seat. In late spring, G.U.E. Tech holds their annual Spelling Bee, which is free and open to the public. The highlight of last year's competition was Magic O'Leary's stunning mastery of clairvoyance spells which allowed him to win the Bee before the first word was even issued.

Every winter, the hills of Borphee come alive with the sound(s) of the most dreadful singers in the Kingdom. This event, aptly named The From Bad to Worst Songfest, allows those truly terrible singers to gain recognition while vying for the much-coveted prize of a pair of 18k gold earplugs. Because most hillside residents schedule out-of-town court appearances or surgery during this two-week period, you may be able to rent an apartment of house for as little as Zm2 or Zm3.5, respectively.

On the official first day of summer, thousands gather st the Borphee Harbor for the G.U.E. Festival of Small Ships.

Throughout the day, hundreds of these floating antiques drop their mini-anchors in the water and send off rockets, flairs and fireworks to herald their safe arrival. Only those spectators 4 feet 5 inches and under will be allowed to board the ships. Admission is free so come early to beat the crowds.

**FACTS:**
**Population:** 1,107,810
**Land Area:** 754 square bloits
**Capital:** Borphee
**Nickname:** The Industrial Province
**Flower:** The Compass Rose
**Motto:** "Borphee—fixum rixa poo nastik"
("Borphee—better than you think")

# THE FRIGID RIVER VALLEY

**LOCAL GOVERNMENT:** None to speak of.

**TRANSPORTATION:** Unless you travel via flying carpet, you'll find this region to be virtually cut off from the rest of the Empire. You can hack your way east through the coastal forests with a machete, or try to cross the Flathead Mountains from the east, or you can try to travel up the Frigid River, bucking the most severe currents and dangerous rapids known to man. We suggest air travel.

**WEATHER:** Very unpredictable, but you'll probably be spending most of your time underground.

**LODGING:** The Tunnels of Love are a favorite of the Kingdom's honeymooners, located a stone's throw from Aragain Falls. The Tunnels are well-known for their vast honeycomb of passageways, and couples have been known to raise entire families just trying to find their rooms. Rates range from Zm2 for a room to Zm10 for a Honeymoon Suite. The Cliffhouse, near White Cliffs Beach, is inexpensive (all rooms are Zm2) and convenient to the big tourist spots.

**DINING:** The Roundup, just off the Round Room, specializes in dragon dishes. Entrees range from Zm0.30 to Zm0.80. The Aqueduct offers reasonably good cuisine and a breathtaking view of one of the Empire's primary water channels. Slightly overpriced at Zm1.20 to Zm2.20.

**THINGS TO SEE:** Flood Control Dam Number Three is a staggering engineering feat that must be seen to be believed. Nearby is Aragain Falls, the so-called Honeymoon Capital of the Great Underground Empire. Slightly farther away is the Royal Museum, although the three-week security clearance procedure discourages many visitors. If mountain climbing turns you on, the Flathead Mountains offer one of the best challenges anywhere.

**SEASONAL EVENTS:** On the first day of summer, crowds line the banks of the Frigid River for a spectacular sight: the annual opening of the floodgates of FCD Number Three, which lower the water level of the reservoir behind. Frequently, the king himself will be on hand to open the floodgates personally.

**FACTS:**
**Population:** 98,330
**Land Area:** 15,232 square bloits
**Capital:** Aragain
**Nickname:** The Deepest Province
**Flower:** The Budding Fern
**Motto:** "Blippi burz fliggin"
("Dig we must")

# GURTH AND MITHICUS

**LOCAL GOVERNMENT:** An informal board of 13 thousand citizens meets three times each day to settle disputes and ratify the provincial budget.

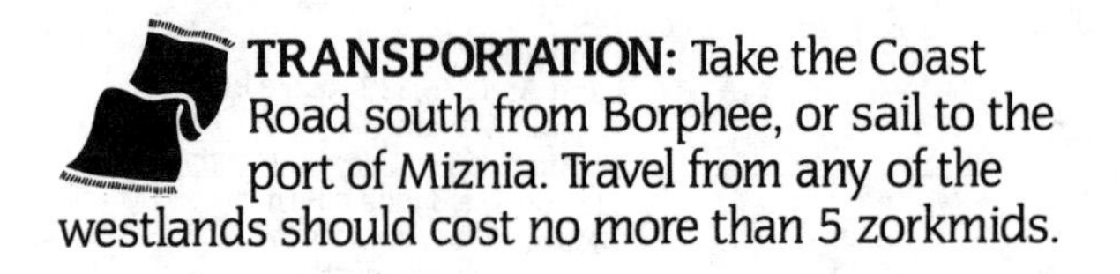

**TRANSPORTATION:** Take the Coast Road south from Borphee, or sail to the port of Miznia. Travel from any of the westlands should cost no more than 5 zorkmids.

**WEATHER:** Absolutely wonderful for most of the year, but it can sometimes get unbearably hot during the peak summer months; bring mosquito netting.

**LODGING:** In Gurth, try the King Zilbo Hotel, an elegant old building with rooms for as little as Zm2.50. Your best bet in Mithicus is the new No-Frill Inn. Rooms are only Zm0.75 per night, but almost everything is extra. (For example, beds are an additional Zm0.50 per night, pillows Zm0.20.)

**DINING:** The Broken Lantern in the village of Grubbo-By-The-Sea serves a fine parrot stew, as well as other local delicacies in an intimate setting. The desserts are world-famous; the morgia root pie is a must. Most meals will be around Zm1.50; desserts are extra.

**THINGS TO SEE:** The southlands are known for their many fine artisans. You can make arrangements at the various guildhalls to see carpenters, woodcarvers, rock cutters, potmakers, and basket weavers at work. The region is also prime vacationland, with many activities to choose from: sky diving, bull-fighting, surfing, skin diving and glurking. Rates vary seasonally, but a day's worth of any of these activities will cost you no more than 2 or 3 zorkmids. Consider exploring the jungles of Miznia, but stay away from the well-marked bloodworm spawning grounds unless you have a trained guide. Trained guides usually start at Zm8 per day.

**SEASONAL EVENTS:** The gigantic Gurth City Crafts Fair is held every weekend during the spring. The finest products of over 80 different guilds are displayed and sold. In early autumn, the annual Harvest Festival gets underway for a colorful two-week celebration featuring local foods, drinks, song and dance.

**FACTS:**
**Population:** 2,883,190
**Land Area:** 21,545 square bloits
**Capital:** Gurth City
**Nickname:** The Vacation Province
**Flower:** The Morgia
**Motto:** "Utribiz oomum flaxil zobs"
("Don't eat moldy bread")

# THE GRAY MOUNTAINS

**LOCAL GOVERNMENT:** Local matters are settled entirely by a tyrannical governor who is chosen once a month by a lottery.

**WEATHER:** Thanks to active hot springs, the temperature of the underground caverns in this region stays at a uniform ideal temperature. However, up on the surface, the temperature is nearly always below freezing, with frequent blizzards.

**TRANSPORTATION:** Travel to this remote area has recently been made much simpler by the completion of the Great Underground Highway's eastern branch. Tolls will run as high as Zm3 depending on your point of departure.

**LODGING:** The brochures for Grayslopes recommend a place called the Ski Pole, but avoid this fleabag at all costs, unless you like bedbugs, rusty water, and rude help. (Apparently, the owners of Grayslopes also own a piece of the Ski Pole.) Instead, stay at the intimate Come-On Inn, which cost only Zm1.30. The Come-On also offers discounts on all equipment rental.

**DINING:** The Glacier Room is a colorful dive which is a favorite hangout for the locals. In addition to generous helpings of good food, the Glacier Room also provides cast rests for diners. From Zm0.60. Warning: ignore recommendations by natives to dine at the Rotgut. Although the locals love to eat there, recommending it to visitors is a practical joke the natives love to play. After all, they've been brought up on this sort of food, plus they know all the best bromide cures.

**THINGS TO SEE:** The hot springs are somewhat overrated as a tourist spot. As far as we're concerned, a trip to the Gray Mountains means one thing: snow sports. A lift ticket at Grayslopes costs Zm3 for a day. Skating on the slanted frozen surface of Lake Dinge is an exhilirating experience. Snow-burrowers rent for around 6 zorkmids per week, but be sure to spend an extra Zm1.50 for a service contract.

**SEASONAL EVENTS:** None. There are no seasons in the Gray Mountains.

**FACTS:**
**Population:** 18,370
**Land Area:** 13,441 square bloits
**Capital:** Frostham
**Nickname:** The Fire and Ice Province
**Flower:** Frobizzan Moss
**Motto:** "Mekie zimbuz"
("Maybe tomorrow")

# Zork III:
# The Dungeon Master

Welcome to Zork!
You are about to experience a classic interactive fantasy, set in a magical universe. The ZORK Trilogy is set in the ruins of an ancient empire lying far underground. You, a dauntless treasure-hunter, are venturing into this dangerous land in search of wealth and adventure. Because each part of the ZORK saga is a completely independent story, you can play them in any order. As Zork III begins, your greatest challenge beckons as you take the final step down into the very heart of the Great Underground Empire. Your character and courage will be tested as the enigmatic Dungeon Master confronts you with predicaments and perils. Your quest hinges upon discovering his secret purpose, even as he oversees your ultimate triumph—or destruction!

## A MESSAGE TO OUR SHAREHOLDERS

778 was a year of continued growth for FrobozzCo and its many subsidiaries. Gross income rose 14% and our revenue increased by 22%. The employment rate now stands at 98.7% for the entire workforce of the Great Underground Empire and is limited only by the birth rate and the size of the Royal Family.

Following the completion of the Royal Museum, the Frobozz Magic Cave Company, our largest subsidiary, moved to increase its staff even more as the well-publicized dam and volcano projects moved into full gear. The Cave Company will also be creating the new 400-story FrobozzCo world headquarters in Flatheadia, scheduled to open sometime in 781.

More than 18,000 additional subsidiaries were formed or taken over during the last year, further increasing the scope of our industrial empire. FrobozzCo now produces everything from aardvarks to zwieback.

I trust that you, as a stockholder, will take the time to read through this report and learn about at least a few of the many exciting things that are going on here at FrobozzCo. It's certainly been a tremendous year, but we're looking forward to an even tremendouser year in 779!

John D. Flathead
President and Chairman of the Board,
FrobozzCo International

# FROBOZZ MAGIC CAVE COMPANY

The first of FrobozzCo's myriad subsidiaries, the Magic Cave Company was formed over a century ago to implement King Duncanthrax's massive tunneling project. Today, the Magic Cave Company is an umbrella for a wide range of underground construction projects.

Two of the most ambitious construction projects ever attempted are now on the Magic Cave Company drawing boards. Construction has already started on a dam of staggering proportions that will span the Frigid River. Tentatively called Flood Control Dam Number Three, the dam is scheduled for completion in 783 G.U.E., and comes with a price tag of 37 million zorkmids.

Magic Cave Company engineers are planning an amazing project to quench and then hollow out a mighty volcano. The project is being conducted under very tight security, and Lord Dimwit Flathead himself is personally reviewing the plans at each stage.

In addition to these landmark projects, the Magic Cave Company created an additional 46,000 linear bloits of tunnel this year, including nearly 200 bloits of the Great Underground Highway extension, as well as 8,000 cubic bloits of additional cavern space.

# FROBOZZ MAGIC TWEEZERS COMPANY

One of the newest and brightest members of the FrobozzCo family, the Magic Tweezers Company was formed after a 652,000-zorkmid market research survey revealed a widespread need for a high-quality technologically advanced tweezer.

Following several years of planning and development, the Frobozz Magic Tweezer Model A-1 is now ready to roll off the assembly lines and into millions of homes all across the Great Underground Empire. The A-1, which will retail for *Zm*0.29, has sold briskly in test markets. Within six months, a top of the line Model X-1 tweezer will be introduced and will retail for *Zm*0.89. Six more models, as well as various add-on accessories, are currently on the drawing board.

The Board of Directors of FrobozzCo welcomes the Frobozz Magic Tweezers Company aboard, and is confident that this new division will pluck a lot of business for the parent conglomerate.

# FROBOZZ MAGIC SPELL COMPANY

While the well-heeled Enchanters Guild remains the primary customer of the Frobozz Magic Spell Company, the invention of self-casting spell scrolls has created a huge new market for magic technology.

Sales increased 11% during 778, marking the twentieth year of steady growth for this lucrative FrobozzCo subsidiary. In response to the growing demand for magic spell accessories, several new FrobozzCo divisions were formed, including the Frobozz Magic Scroll Rack Company, the Frobozz Magic Spell Book Company, and the Frobozz Magic Scroll Mailing Tube Company.

Four new spells were added to the Magic Spell Company product line this year, a Magic Spell Company record and a tribute to the wizards in FrobozzCo's famous Magiclab. The four new spells are DRILBO (strips a floor of yellowed wax), BORCH (puts insects to sleep), GIZGUM (predicts visits by relatives) and QUELBO (transmutes coconuts into gold).

# FROBOZZ MAGIC GRUE REPELLENT COMPANY

The Frobozz Magic Grue Repellent Company is one of FrobozzCo's fastest growing divisions. Sales of grue repellent nearly tripled last year, spurred on by drastic extensive improvements made in the product and by an aggressive marketing campaign. Magic Grue Repellent Company executives can proudly point to a 31% drop in grue-related deaths during the last year, and a consequent 31% drop in the grue population.

The discovery of a particularly effective new additive by the Magic Grue Repellent Company's research division has increased the efficiency of the product by 45%. Studies have shown that most grues will not come within 70 feet of someone sprayed with New Improved Repellent. The new additive, dubbed G-17, is also longer-lasting, requiring fewer sprayings, and it can be made from ordinary sand!

The Magic Grue Repellent Company also increased the product line with the introduction of seven new odors of repellent, in addition to the regular old socks/burning rubber odor. The new odors include rotting eggs, dead fish, swamp gas, three-week-old meatloaf, gym locker, wet dog and mint.

Several ingenious sales strategies were highly successful. The Free-Noseplugs-With-Every-Can campaign, in association with the Frobozz Magic Noseplugs Company, ran for one month and increased sales by 92%. Advertisements featuring grue-mangled corpses ran before and during the peak travel season. Finally, a joint packaging effort with the Frobozz Magic Lantern Company to produce a Frobozz Anti-Grue Kit paid off with remarkable end-of-year sales.

# FROBOZZCO FINANCIAL REPORT

## FrobozzCo International Income Statement
(Zorkmid Amounts in Millions)

| | Year end 778 | Year end 777 |
|---|---|---|
| **Revenues:** | | |
| Sales of goods and services | *Zm*5,431,922 | *Zm*5,108,113 |
| Sale of property | 350,585 | ---- |
| Other revenues | 812,913 | 656,106 |
| TOTAL REVENUES | 6,595,420 | 5,764,219 |
| **Expenses:** | | |
| Cost of goods and services | 2,773,119 | 2,655,288 |
| Selling, administration, bribes | 1,243,984 | 1,256,712 |
| Depreciation | 127,353 | 112,499 |
| Contributions to Royal Charities | 888,307 | 888,307 |
| Printing of Annual Report | 285,238 | 279,540 |
| TOTAL EXPENSES | 5,318,001 | 5,192,346 |
| **NET INCOME** | *Zm*1,277,419 | *Zm* 571,873 |
| Earnings per uncommon share: | | |
| Continuing operations | *Zm* 2.72 | *Zm* 1.54 |
| Discontinuing operations | (0.03) | (0.02) |
| **NET INCOME PER UNCOMMON SHARE** | *Zm* 2.69 | *Zm* 1.52 |

## FrobozzCo International Retained Earnings Statement
(Zorkmid Amounts in Millions)

| | Year end 778 | Year end 777 |
|---|---|---|
| Retained earnings at year opening | *Zm*1,204,445 | *Zm*1,162,556 |
| Net income | 1,277,419 | 571,873 |
| Dividends paid on uncommon stock | (894,017) | (529,971) |
| Dividends paid on unpreferred stock | (24) | (13) |
| Retained earnings at year end | *Zm*1,587,823 | *Zm*1,204,445 |

## FrobozzCo International Balance Sheet
(Zorkmid Amounts in Millions)

| | Year end 778 | Year end 777 |
|---|---|---|
| **Assets:** | | |
| Cash | *Zm* 393,459 | *Zm* 219,067 |
| Inventories | 566,790 | 465,634 |
| Loans to Royal Family | 1,125,000 | 900,000 |
| Executive Party Fund | 107,374 | 135,252 |
| Plant and Equipment | 778,833 | 596,025 |
| Other assets | 325,939 | 294,606 |
| **TOTAL ASSETS** | *Zm*3,297,395 | *Zm*2,610,584 |
| **Liabilities:** | | |
| Short term loans | *Zm* 456,872 | 388,431 |
| Accrued payroll deductions | 594,311 | 435,923 |
| Deferred bribes | 216,343 | 209,575 |
| Other liabilities | 95,647 | 80,293 |
| Total Liabilities | 1,363,173 | 1,114,222 |
| Shareholder's equity: | | |
| Uncommon stock | 345,287 | 291,054 |
| Unpreferred stock | 1,112 | 858 |
| Retained earnings | 1,587,823 | 1,204,445 |
| Total shareholder's equity | 1,934,222 | 1,496,357 |
| **TOTAL LIABILITIES AND EQUITY** | *Zm*3,297,395 | *Zm*2,610,579 |

# Beyond Zork

Preface to the Story
Dark times have fallen upon the South lands of Quendor. All the enchanters have disappeared without a trace. Monsters roam the country-side. And the taverns are filled with disturbing rumors and un-savory characters. A simple peasant like yourself knows better than to get involved in the affairs of wizards. But everyone you meet seems intent on testing your abilities to the utmost. You find yourself drawn into a web of fantasy and magic, solving puzzles, avoiding traps and fighting monsters. Your strength and power grow with every encounter, until the most fabulous treasure of all - the fabled Coconut of Quendor - lies within your grasp. If only you can survive long enough to claim it! Unlike other Infocom stories in which your character is "set" from the start, Beyond Zork lets you create your own character with six attributes: endurance, strength, dexterity, intelligence, compassion and luck. Each attribute affects your adventure in different ways. For example, a very lucky character may not have the dexterity to scale walls, or a very intelligent character may be able to outsmart a monster that even a strong character couldn't defeat. You can choose your attributes yourself, or you can use a character already set up by the computer. You must fight monsters and solve puzzles to succeed in each of your quests. Since your success will often depend on your attributes, mindful players will try to improve their attributes as they venture onward. The story is presented in a new and flexible way. A map in the upper-right portion of your screen shows the immediate area and the directions you can move. You can use the on-screen map and your mouse to move to adjacent rooms. (If your computer has a numeric keypad, you can use it to move around as well.) Experienced Infocom players may recognize references to other Infocom games.

About the Author
"Professor" Brian Moriarty built his first computer in the fifth grade. This early experience with electronics led him to seek a degree in English Literature at Southeastern Massachusetts University, where he graduated in 1978. He is a member in good standing of the Nathaniel Hawthorne Society, and accepts full responsibility for his previous Infocom titles, Wishbringer and Trinity.

**Beyond Zork Special Commands**

*COLOR - If you are playing Beyond Zork on a computer with a color monitor, you can type COLOR to change the colors on your screen. This command works only on some computers.

*DEFINE - This command allows you to change the settings of the function keys. For example, if pressing function key 2 is like typing INVENTORY, you can change this to DROP ALL, or DROP ALL followed by RETURN (or ENTER), or anything else, by using the DEFINE command.

*MODE - If you find the maps and other screen features of Beyond Zork undesirable, you can use the MODE command. This will make the screen look "standard," like every other Infocom game. Typing MODE a second time will cause the "enhanced" screen features to return.

*MONITOR - Your character's endurance attribute is especially important. Therefore, whenever something affects your endurance (being wounded during combat, for example), your endurance level is automatically displayed on the screen. If for some reason you do not wish to monitor your endurance, use the MONITOR command. Typing MONITOR a second time turns the endurance-display feature back on.

*NAME - In Beyond Zork, you have the power to name weapons and living things. For instance, you can NAME THE DOG "ROVER" or NAME THE SWORD "EXCALIBUR" or NAME THE HIPPOPOTAMUS "FRED". Beyond Zork will then use the name in its descriptions, and you can use the name as a synonym form the object. This feature is particularly convenient when an unnamed object is long or hard to spell.

*NOTIFY - Normally in Beyond Zork, the game will notify you whenever any of your attributes change (for example, when your luck goes up or when you dexterity goes down) or when any attribute returns to normal (such as when you build your strength back after being wounded in battle). You can turn off this notification feature by using the NOTIFY command. Typing NOTIFY a second time turns the feature back on.

*OOPS - If you accidentally mistype a word, such that Beyond Zork doesn't understand the word, you can correct yourself on the next line by typing OOPS and the correct word. Suppose, for example, you typed TAKE THE CLUB FROM THE GIANT and were told "[I don't know the word 'giant.']" You could type OOPS GIANT rather than retyping the entire sentence.

*PRIORITY - As you play Beyond Zork, most information is displayed in a box at the top half of your screen. For instance, when you enter a new room, the room's description will appear in the box; when you then type INVENTORY, your inventory will appear in the box; on some machines, when you type STATUS, your attributes will appear in the box. If you want, you can specify what kind of information appears in the box by using the PRIORITY command. For example, if you want the box to show your inventory at all times, type INVENTORY and then type PRIORITY; thereafter the box will always show your inventory, updating it when you pick up new items or drop or lose others. (Room descriptions will thereafter appear in the bottom half of the screen.) Similarly, if you want the box to show room descriptions at all times, type LOOK and then type PRIORITY. You can turn this feature off by typing PRIORITY OFF.

**Be sure to use the "Southland of Quendor" map in the Map packet included in "The Lost Treasure" box.**

# The Lore and Legends of Quendor

## Infocom

Within these pages is recorded certain knowledge regarding the flora, fauna, and locales of the kingdom. Although this wisdom has well stood the test of time, I would not wish to see it lost forever in the uncertain mists of the future. Therefore, for the enrichment of our heirs and with homage to our ancestors, I have writ into permanence the lore and legends of Quendor.

—MNG

## GRUE

The grue is a sinister, lurking presence in the dark places of the earth. Its favorite diet is adventurers, but its insatiable appetite is tempered by its fear of light. No grue has ever been seen by the light of day; few have survived its fearsome jaws to tell the tale.

## DISCIPLINE CRAB

Discipline crabs are small, moral crustaceans found in cellars, fallout shelters and other subterranean lairs. These brooding curmudgeons are deeply offended by the slightest intrusion; if cornered, they employ their razor-edged pincers with righteous efficiency.

## ELDRITCH VAPOR

Eldritch vapors dwell in cemeteries, moors and other locales where fog will hide their evershifting forms. Gleeful and mischievous, they enjoy snatching away the possessions of those foolish enough to wander into their realm. Visitors without possessions are themselves snatched away.

## DORNBEAST

Smart adventurers run the other way when they hear "Hurumph," the battle cry of the deadly dornbeast. Its 69 sensitive eyes can paralyze an unwary explorer with a single glare. Captured victims are plastered with round, sticky secretions that never come off.

## MONKEY GRINDER

Avoid this nightmare at any cost! Spawn of a carnival necromancer, the monkey grinder can blast minds to jelly with its powerful Sense Organ. Deceptively eloquent in both manner and speech, these loathsome creatures actually possess little intelligence, and suffer an illiteracy rate of 103%.

## IMPLEMENTOR

The Implementors are a race of minor deities who dwell on the Ethereal Plane of Atrii. Their ample free time is spent on costly luncheons where gossip and sweet nectars flow freely. Implementors do not discourage rumors that the world was created by them as a plaything.

## GIANT CORBIE

Corbies are carrion birds with sharp eyesight and sharper beaks. Their color vision is so well developed, they can spot a yellow grotch in a hayfield from 200 bloits away. Corbies prefer the taste of dead, rotting flesh, but have been known to feast on live, running adventurers.

## CHRISTMAS TREE MONSTER

Vast herds of these luminous vegetables roam freely amid the glacial valleys of the south. Residents fear the autumn migrations, in which the trees cheerfully trample everything in their path. Christmas tree monsters are repelled by caterpillars, but nobody can explain why.

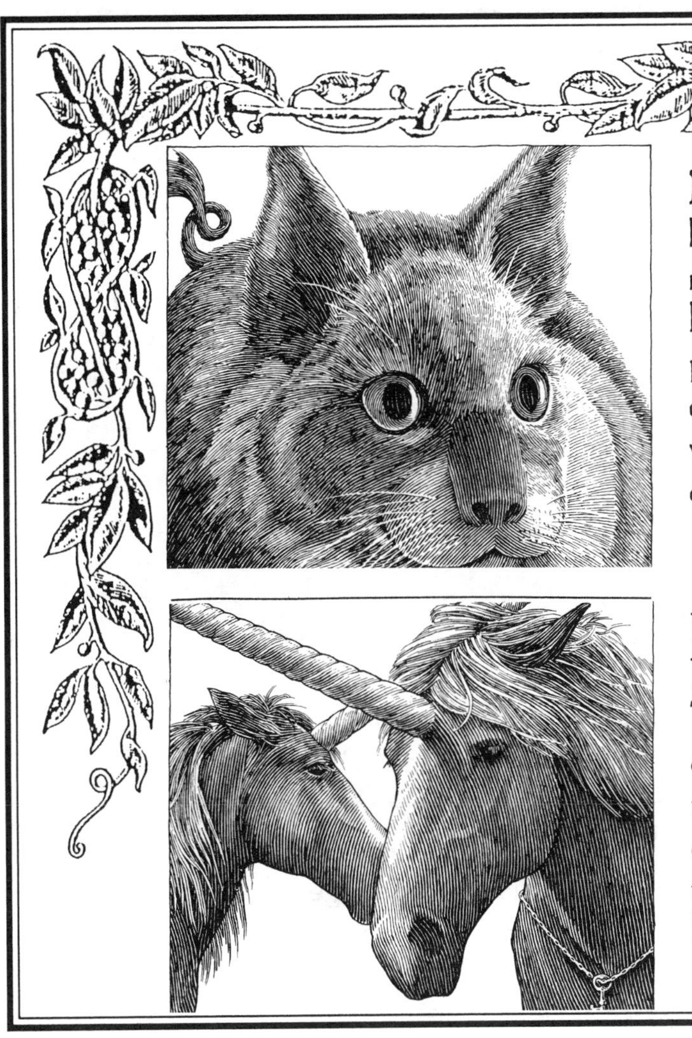

## MINX

Irresistably cuddly, the minx shares all the most ingratiating characteristics of kittens, koala bears and piglets. Minxes are highly prized for their ability to find and root out chocolate truffles from the ground, and will eagerly devour them if given the opportunity.

## UNICORN

Most unicorns have fled to the Plane of TransInfinite Splendor, where they enjoy a carefree existence free from the cruelty of man. The unhappy few left behind are eagerly sought by zoos and private collectors. It is good luck to kiss a unicorn's horn; but woe to any fool who harms one.

## FROON

Legends of this magical kingdom date back before the reign of Entharion the Wise (0-41 GUE). Said to lie somewhere beyond the clouds, Froon was the setting for a series of beloved children's books by L. Frank Fzort, and later became a successful movie musical starring Judy Garlic.

## HUNGUS

Part sheep, part hippopotamus, the hungus builds its nest in jungle swamps and other hot, squishy places. Normally docile and eager to avoid conflict or activity of any kind, the hungus is fiercely clannish, and will instantly charge at anything that dares to threaten its kin.

## SPENSEWEED

The healing virtues of this common roadside plant are well documented. Although it is safe to eat, spenseweed is most effective when applied directly to wounds as a salve. Avoid the cheap commercial preparations, which may contain artificial coloring and preservatives.

## CHOCOLATE TRUFFLE

Chocolate truffles grow only between the roots of oak trees. Dark brown when fresh, they decompose rapidly once exposed to air. Truffles were a favorite of Lord Dimwit Flathead the Excessive (770-789 GUE), who ordered the excavation of entire forests to indulge his bottomless appetite.

## MOSS OF MAREILON

First classified in 843 GUE by Thwack of Mareilon, this soft, pale fungus thrives in underground tunnels and public toilets. When squeezed, the moss releases an invisible cloud of spores which improves the dexterity of laboratory rat-ants. Its effect on other species is uncertain.

## COMPASS ROSE

The stem of this rare annual always droops in the direction of the prevailing wind. Rumors that the compass rose can actually control the wind are hotly denied by the Guild of Meteorologists, who harvested the species to the brink of extinction in the Rose Riots of 811 GUE.

## MORGIA ROOT

It is a rare enchanter who does not carry morgia root to gnaw on during a long journey. The mint-flavored juice improves stamina, slakes thirst and conceals bad breath. In domestic applications, morgia root is often baked into pies, and makes an excellent platypus stuffing.

## CRUEL PUPPET

Few creatures are more despised than the cruel puppet. It attacks by twisting itself into unflattering caricatures of its opponent, accompanied by jeers, rude noises and shocking accusations. Staunch monarchs have been reduced to tears by these merciless shapeshifters.

## DUST BUNNY

Dust bunnies burrow in obscure corners and under furniture, and defend their territory by multiplying. They can clog a passageway in seconds, filling the air with dark, suffocating particles. Static electricity and lemon-scented sprays are their only natural enemies.

## PHEEBOR

Ruins of this ancient city are still visible at the confluence of the rivers Phee and Bor. The reason for its downfall (circa 400 BE) is unclear, but minstrels sing of a feud between Pheebor and its sister city Borphee over the naming of what is now called the Borphee River.

## RED HERRING

These common fish patrol the dark recesses of freshwater pools and streams. But a handful of granola brings them racing to the surface, a fact known by every rural schoolboy. The old adage about red herrings being "good brain food" has no scientific basis.

## LUCKSUCKER

Lucksuckers feed on good fortune. Part physical entity, part mental phenomenon, the sucker's appearance is based on the laws of probability, and may change without warning. Good luck charms provide only a temporary shield against attack. The best strategy is to run!

## UR-GRUE

Ur-grues are thought to be the shades of fallen Implementors. Skilled in black sorcery, the ur-grue can envelop itself in a personal zone of darkness which neither lamp nor flame can penetrate. Sunlight is the only thing it fears. It is unwise even to speak of this utterly evil entity.

## THE COCONUT OF QUENDOR

Though reluctant to dismiss the Coconut outright, most historians regard its historical existence as dubious at best. Orkan of Thriff has suggested that if all the "Shards of The One True Coconut" and "Vials of The Blessed Milk" were gathered in one place, they would form a stack nine bloits high.

# Zork Zero

Preface to the Story

More than 90 years have passed since the great wizard Megaboz cast the Curse which destroyed Lord Dimwit Flathead the Excessive along with the other members of the ruling family, the Twelve Flatheads. Now, the Curse threatens to bring down the Great Underground Empire itself! Wurb Flathead, the current occupant of the throne, has sent a clarion call to the remotest corners of the Empire: half the riches of the kingdom to the person who can allay the Curse. From every province of Quendor, courageous adventurers, scheming charlatans, and wild-eyed crackpots have streamed into the Imperial Capital of Flatheadia. You are one such treasure-seeker, a peasant from an unheard-of village in an obscure province. However, you have an important advantage: an ancestor of yours, a servant in Dimwit's court, witnessed Megaboz casting the Curse, and obtained a small scrap of wizardly parchment from the mage's pocket. This parchment scrap has been passed down from generation to generation, and is now in your possession. Thanks to it, you know what none of the other would-be cursebusters know; you alone know what must be done to stop the Curse! By the time of your arrival at Flatheadia, most of the treasure-seekers have given up and returned to their homelands. In fact, you discover that most of the population, including all figures of authority, have fled to distant provinces. And when you awake on the hard floor of the castle on Curse Day, you find that even the looters and the most persistent adventurers have departed. In fact, as you begin your desperate quest to find the relics of the Empire you need to stop the Curse, your only company is the court jester, who spins rhymes for your amusement. Always appearing when you least expect him, the jester will confront you with riddles and games, spring some deadly tricks, and give you helpful nudges in the right direction. And throughout, he seems to be laughing at some tremendous joke which you can't begin to fathom...

Zork Zero is the prequel to the Zork Trilogy, one of the most popular, best-loved computer games ever written. Zork Zero takes you back to the age of the Flatheads, where you can glimpse the Great Underground Empire during its heyday, and witness its monumental fall.

About the Author : Steve Meretzky (1957- ) was born and raised in Yonkers, NY, where his early hobbies included rooting for the New York Mets and against Richard Nixon. A few historians of interactive fiction think that Meretzky's first job, packing nuts and bolts for his father's hardware business, was the formative moment of his writing career. A few other people think that there's absolutely no connection. Most people don't think about it at all. Many have won awards, but probably no awards you've ever heard of. Along with Infocom's Dave Lebling, Meretzky is the first person admitted to the Science Fiction Writers of America for authoring interactive fiction. Other works of interactive fiction by Steve Meretzky: Planetfall (1983), Sorcerer (1984), The Hitchhiker's Guide to the Galaxy (1984) (with Douglas Adams), A Mind Forever Voyaging (1985), Leather Goddesses of Phobos (1986), Stationfall (1987)

**Zork Zero Special Commands**

*COLOR - If you are playing Zork Zero on a computer with a color monitor, you can type COLOR to change the colors of the text and background on your screen. This command works only on computers which support a color display.

*DEFINE - This command allows you to change the settings of the function keys. For example, if pressing function key 2 is like typing INVENTORY, you can change this to DROP ALL, or DROP ALL followed by RETURN (or ENTER), or anything else, by using the DEFINE command. See the "Function Keys" section on page N.

*HINT - If you have difficulty while playing the story, and you can't figure out what to do, just type HINT. Then follow the directions at the top of your screen to read the hint of your choice.

*NOTIFY - Normally in Zork Zero, the game will notify you whenever your score changes. You can turn off this notification feature by using the NOTIFY command. Typing NOTIFY pa second time turns the feature back on.

*OOPS - If you mistype a word, such that Zork Zero doesn't understand it, you can correct yourself at the next prompt by typing OOPS and the correct word. For example, if you typed HAND THE CHAIN SAW TO GARNDMA .and were told "[I don't know the word 'garndma'"] you could type OOPS GRANDMA rather than retyping the entire sentence You can abbreviate OOPS to O.

*REFRESH - This command clears your screen and redraws the display.

*UNDO - You can use this command to "back up" one move. Suppose, for example, that you found a package but didn't know what was in it. You might type OPEN THE PACKAGE .and be told "The package explodes as you open it, destroying all your possessions." You could then type .UNDO, and you would "back up" one move. Your possessions would be intact, and you could try giving the package to an enemy, or leaving it alone, or something else. Note that the UNDO command works only on certain computers with enough memory.

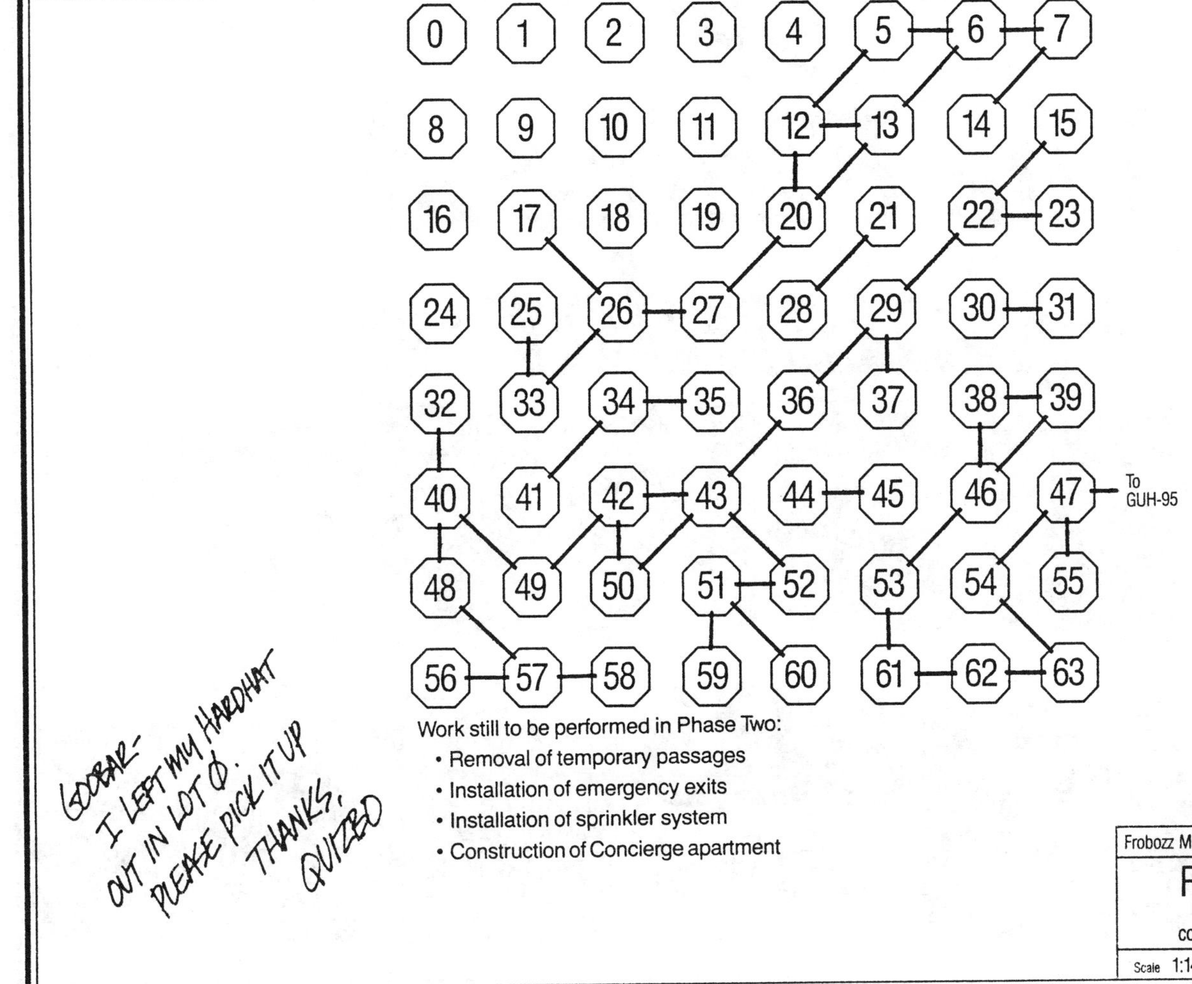


Work still to be performed in Phase Two:

- Removal of temporary passages
- Installation of emergency exits
- Installation of sprinkler system
- Construction of Concierge apartment

| Frobozz Magic Construction Company | 1 of 1 |
|---|---|
| **Rockville Estates**<br>Phase Two, showing all work completed through 29-Mum-880 | |
| Scale 1:1440 | drawn by S. Fzortbar |

# The Flathead Calendar

# 883

# THE TWELVE FLATHEADS

*As every student of history knows, the Twelve Flatheads were the greater part of the Thirteen Significant Accomplishments of King Mumberthrax the Insignificant.**

*In the immortal words of Boswell Barwell, the royal biographer:*

Mumberthrax's place in history was secured by the one thing at which the Flatheads tended to excel: procreation. He sired twelve amazing children; twelve offspring who would transform the kingdom. As these magnificent siblings grew in notoriety, as their vast achievements became legendary, they became known as The Twelve Flatheads.**

*In 783 GUE, the coronation of Lord Dimwit Flathead the Excessive, Mumberthrax's firstborn, began at Flatheadia. This calendar, brought to you under the auspices of the Flatheadia Chamber of Commerce and the Frobozz Magic Calendar Company, celebrates the centennial of that memorable occasion.*

*Reproduced for this calendar are Leonardo Flathead's famous portraits of the Twelve Flatheads.*** Leonardo brilliantly captured the varied personalities of the siblings on canvas over a span of seventeen years, starting with his own self-portrait in 766 GUE (see Jelly) and finishing with his Coronation Portrait of King Dimwit in 783 GUE (see Estuary).*

*We are grateful for permission to reprint the accompanying excerpts from Boswell Barwell's exhaustive biography, "The Lives of the Twelve Flatheads."*****

*The thirteenth accomplishment was a decree that made Double Fanucci the National Sport of Quendor. Legends say that Double Fanucci was invented by Zilbo III, the last king of the Entharion dynasty. Double Fanucci Championships had been an annual event since 691 GUE, and Mumberthrax's Proclamation of 757 simply gave the sport official royal approval.*

***From the introduction to "The Lives of the Twelve Flatheads."*

****The originals can be seen in the gallery at Flatheadia Castle. Acknowledgement is gratefully made to Winifred Booblort of the Flatheadia Castle Preservation Society for her invaluable help.*

*****Copied right in 804 GUE by the Frobozz Magic Biography Publishing Company.*

# DIMWIT FLATHEAD

## Excessive Ruler of the Empire
## (723–789)

Dimwit, as Mumberthrax's firstborn, grew up as heir to the throne of Quendor. A tad spoiled, little Dimmie was fond of torturing his nannies in the castle dungeon.

Dimwit spent most of his early adulthood vacationing (with 40,000 attendants) in the sparsely populated Eastlands across the Great Sea. Dimwit, who despised the outdoors,* was enthralled by the underground caverns there.

When Mumberthrax felt death's icy hand in 770 GUE, Dimwit began his vibrant reign. He immediately moved the capital of Quendor from Egreth, in the Westlands, to Aragain, in the Eastlands. Aragain, a small village, was transformed and renamed Flatheadia. Dimwit also decreed that Quendor be called "The Great Underground Empire."**

Dimwit's grandiosity knew no bounds. His wondrous coronation ceremony*** quickly earned him the nickname Lord Dimwit Flathead the Excessive. On a whim, in 783, he ordered the erection of Flood Control Dam #3, an underground project whose uselessness and cost did not diminish its magnificence. He also had huge granola smelters built near the Antharian Granola Mines.

Some bitter, unappreciative chroniclers have described Dimwit's castle as his biggest folly. It covered 8,600 square bloits, and housed, at one time, over 90% of the empire's population.

Dimwit's last great project was the erection of a huge statue of himself in the Fublio Valley. Nine bloits tall, it necessitated the deforestation of 1,400 square bloits.

It was rumored that Dimwit was planning the construction of a new continent in the Flathead Ocean; a continent whose contours would have resembled his own features. Sadly, Dimwit passed away in 789 before he could realize this incomparable goal. His death has always been shrouded in mystery.

**Dimwit was petrified of rain, which puddled embarrassingly on his level pate.*

***Nowadays, these names are used interchangeably.*

****The ceremony took thirteen years to plan and lasted eighteen fun-filled months.*

# ESTUARY 883

| Sand Day | Mud Day | Grues Day | Wands Day | Birthday | Frob Day™ | Star Day |
|---|---|---|---|---|---|---|
| 1 *Entharion Day* | 2 | 3 Mom's Birthday | 4 | 5 *Dimwit's Birthday Observed* | 6 | 7 |
| 8 | 9 | 10 | 11 | 12 *Dimwit's Birthday Observed* | 13 | 14 |
| 15 | 16 *Granola Riots (865 GUE)* | 17 | 18 *Endless Fire started (773 GUE)* | 19 *Dimwit's Birthday Observed* | 20 | 21 |
| 22 NEW MOON | 23 | 24 | 25 | 26 *Dimwit's Birthday Observed* | 27 | 28 |
| 29 | 30 *Flood Control Dam #3 dedicated (783 GUE)* | 31 | **DID U KNOW?** Dimwit's Birthday, now associated with big sales at U-Mart and J.C. Zorkmids, was once a day when everyone in the kingdom was required to give the king a present. | | | |

*Frob Day is a traderune of the Frobozz Magic Day Company.*

# JOHN D. FLATHEAD

## Captain of Industry

## (725–789)

King Duncanthrax formed the Frobozz Magic Construction Company in 667 GUE to enlarge the underground caverns of the Eastlands. Affiliated companies, such as the Frobozz Magic Dirt Disposal Company, and the Frobozz Magic Underground Sewer Installation Company, soon followed. The next year, FrobozzCo International was formed as a parent company for the burgeoning subsidiaries.

By 743, there were more than 17,000 subsidiaries of FrobozzCo. That same year, a young entrepreneur named John D. Flathead graduated from the venerable Borphee Business School.

At age 22, John D. founded Flathead Industries. FI's business was inventing other companies, which it would then sell to FrobozzCo. Within three years, FI had an annual income of 80,000,000 zorkmids. Eventually, the conglomerate decided to buy FI, renaming it the Frobozz Magic Company Company. John D. became one of FrobozzCo's 39,000 vice-presidents.

It didn't take John D. long to parlay his business acumen and royal connections into the chairmanship of FrobozzCo. Years of heady growth followed. When John D.'s older brother Dimwit became king, FrobozzCo received every contract for Dimwit's incredible projects. Hundreds of new subsidiaries were formed daily; in 781 a huge 400-story headquarters opened in Flatheadia.

John D.'s long-time goal was for FrobozzCo to control every single zorkmid of commerce in the Great Underground Empire. The lone holdout, a small rutabaga farm in Mithicus, finally sold out to FrobozzCo in 789. John D. never heard the news, however. He disappeared, along with a huge entourage, while touring the factories of the Frobozz Magic Snowmaking Equipment Company in the Gray Mountains.

# FROBUARY[TR] 883

| Sand Day | Mud Day | Grues Day | Wands Day | Birthday | Frob Day[TR] | Star Day |
|---|---|---|---|---|---|---|
| **FUN FAX** Frobuary[TR] was originally called Fidooshiary until it was purchased by the Frobozz Magic Month Company in 817 GUE. | | | 1 | 2 (moon phase) *Dimwit's Birthday Observed* | 3 *Undergroundhog's Day* | 4 |
| 5 | 6 | 7 | 8 | 9 *Dimwit's Birthday Observed* | 10 | 11 (moon phase) |
| 12 | 13 | 14 | 15 | 16 *Dimwit's Birthday Observed* | 17 | 18 |
| 19 | 20 FULL MOON | 21 | 22 | 23 *Dimwit's Birthday Observed* | 24 | 25 |
| 26 / 33 | 27 / 34 | 28 / 35 | 29 (moon phase) *Start of Leap Week (Antharia only)* | 30 *Dimwit's Birthday Observed* | 31 | 32 |

*Frob Day is a traderune of the Frobozz Magic Day Company.*
*Frobuary is a traderune of the Frobozz Magic Month Company.*

# STONEWALL FLATHEAD

## Military Hero
## (726–789)

T.J. "Stonewall" Flathead received his celebrated nickname while serving as a Squire in the Royal Army during the famous Battle of The Stonewall in 747 GUE.

The Stonewall was a strategically vital locale, commanding the two most important caverns of the Eastlands. When reports arrived that rebellious natives had captured The Stonewall, T.J. Flathead and his garrison were assigned the mission of retaking it.

After a battle lasting seven weeks, during which T.J.'s men suffered a casualty rate of nearly 75%, the garrison stormed The Stonewall. Once in command of it, they discovered that the reports had been erroneous: The Stonewall was completely undefended, and the supposedly rebellious natives were actually all vacationing in the Gray Mountains. Nevertheless, T.J.'s tactics and strategies during the battle were brilliant, and he would henceforth be known as Stonewall Flathead.

Stonewall rose quickly through the ranks, and in 755 GUE he became General of the Royal Army.

During his 34 years in command, he squelched three provincial rebellions and over 12,000 tax riots. Fortunately, his unlimited conscription powers helped mitigate the 98% casualty rates his army suffered during these difficult battles.

Stonewall died in 789 GUE during the Battle of Ragweed Gulch, when he was accidentally shot by one of his own men.

# ARCH 883

| Sand Day | Mud Day | Grues Day | Wands Day | Birthday | Frob Day™ | Star Day |
|---|---|---|---|---|---|---|
| **KRAZY KWOTES** "Why pay less?" –Dimwit Flathead | | | 1 | 2 *Dimwit's Birthday Observed* | 3 | 4 |
| 5 | 6 | 7 | 8 | 9 *Dimwit's Birthday Observed* | 10 | 11 *St. Balhu's Day* |
| 12 | 13 | 14 | 15 | 16 *Dimwit's Birthday Observed* | 17 | 18 |
| 19 *Frobozz Magic Cave Co. founded (668 GUE)* | 20 | 21 EMPTY MOON | 22 *Royal Museum dedicated (777 GUE)* | 23 *Dimwit's Birthday Observed* | 24 | 25 |
| 26 | 27 | 28 | 29 | 30 *Dimwit's Birthday Observed* | 31 | |

*Frob Day is a traderune of the Frobozz Magic Day Company.*

# JOHANN SEBASTIAN FLATHEAD

## Musical Genius

## (728–789)

In 732 GUE, the Frobozz Philharmonic Orchestra was formed. Because of the woeful lack of orchestral music in existence, the FPO usually settled for playing baroque versions of old folk tunes and popular dance numbers.

Seven years later, the FPO performed their first symphony. The piece was notable because of the age of its author, a precocious eleven-year-old named Johann Sebastian Flathead.

As he matured, Johann's symphonies increased in length, while his audiences mysteriously decreased in size.* His Symphony #981, the so-called Infinite Symphony, contained over 60,000 movements; over the course of its only performance, several members of the orchestra retired and were replaced by their children or grandchildren.

Dimwit recognized a kindred spirit in his younger brother, and appointed him official court composer in 771. Later that year, he wrote his famous "Flatheadia Overture for Rack and Pendulum" to celebrate the dedication of Dimwit's new dungeon.

He spent his latter years composing music for ever more grandiose instruments, such as his Concerto for Woodwinds and Waterfalls. Johann was killed in 789 when a mishap occurred during a rehearsal of his Minuet for Violin and Volcano.

**No reasonable postulation has been made to explain Johann's lack of popularity. It is the belief of this author that the short attention span of the general public precluded it from sitting still for the whole of one of his symphonies.*

# ORACLE 883

| Sand Day | Mud Day | Grues Day | Wands Day | Birthday | Frob Day™ | Star Day |
|---|---|---|---|---|---|---|
| **TID BITZ** This year is the 100th anniversary of the original Coronation Day. Since Dimwit's coronation, all subsequent kings have been crowned on Oracle 22nd. | | | | | | 1 |
| 2 | 3<br>*King Wurb's Birthday* | 4<br>*St. Foobus' Day* | 5 | 6<br>*Dimwit's Birthday Observed* | 7 | 8 |
| 9 | 10 | 11 | 12 | 13<br>*Dimwit's Birthday Observed* | 14 | 15 |
| 16 | 17 | 18 | 19 | 20<br>*Dimwit's Birthday Observed* | 21 | 22<br>Coronation Day |
| 23<br>30 | 24 | 25 | 26<br>OLD MOON | 27<br>*Dimwit's Birthday Observed* | 28 | 29<br>dinner at the Bozbo's |

*Frob Day is a traderune of the Frobozz Magic Day Company.*

# J. PIERPONT FLATHEAD
## Dauntless Banker and Financier
## (730–789)

As a child, J. Pierpont demonstrated both the flair for capitalism and the resourcefulness which would make him the most successful banker in all of Quendor. The enterprising eight-year-old opened a lemonade stand in the center of Egreth Village, using the royal militia to force citizens to buy lemonade. At spearpoint, most people were willing to pay little J. Pierpont's exorbitant price of 300 zorkmids per glass.*

He also used the militia to quash the other lemonade stands in the city, and later to shut off all other beverage sources as well. As the prices at his lemonade stand soared into quadruple digits, J. Pierpont quickly realized the benefits of monopolies.

In 749, at the age of nineteen, J. Pierpont became a clerk at the Bank of Zork. Six weeks later, following a rash of disappearances of his successive bosses, J. Pierpont became the youngest Chairman of the Board in the bank's history, a testament to his financial acumen.

As Chairman, he used his royal connections to eliminate all competing banks, increasing the Bank of Zork's market share from 99.2% to 100%.** He also supervised the installation of the latest magic-based security techniques to guard the bank's vault and deposit box areas. For unknown reasons, J. Pierpont hired exclusively gnomes to fill his teller and security positions.

J. Pierpont Flathead served as Chairman of the Board until his odd disappearance in 789 GUE, when he entered one of the bank's vaults and never re-emerged. Although gone, he is not forgotten; reproductions of his portrait still hang in every branch of the Bank of Zork.

**Ice was extra.*

***He was later able to increase this number to 131% by encouraging customers to deposit their money several times.*

# MAGE 883

| Sand Day | Mud Day | Grues Day | Wands Day | Birthday | Frob Day[TR] | Star Day |
|---|---|---|---|---|---|---|
| 0 *Zero Day* | 1 *Mage Day* | 2 | 3 | 4 *Dimwit's Birthday Observed* | 5 | 6 *Antharian Marble Pageant* |
| 7 | 8 | 9 | 10 | 11 *Dimwit's Birthday Observed* | 12 | 13 |
| 14 | 15 | 16 | 17 | 18 *Dimwit's Birthday Observed* | 19 | 20 |
| 21 | 22 | 23 | 24 | 25 *Dimwit's Birthday Observed* | 26 PAC MOON | 27 |
| 28 | 29 | 30 | 31 *St. Honko's Day* | **QUICKIE QUIZ** Who was the first king in the Flathead Dynasty? | | |

*Frob Day is a traderune of the Frobozz Magic Day Company.*

## THOMAS ALVA FLATHEAD
### Inventor Extraordinaire
### (730–789)

Many have mastered the magical arts; few applied them to the creation of practical devices as masterfully as the great inventor Thomas Alva Flathead.

His brilliance was evident even in childhood. Thomas Alva, the sixth son in his family, was constantly tormented by his siblings: no sooner would he get a toy to play with than some older brother would snatch it away. Thomas Alva quickly remedied the situation by inventing powerful steel traps which, at first glance, looked exactly like toy boats or stuffed dornbeasts.

As an adult, Thomas Alva produced a seemingly endless stream of inventions from his laboratory, Froblo Park. His most useful inventions include the magic room spinner and the magic compressor, but he is probably best-known as the inventor of the battery-powered brass lantern.

Thomas Alva also made a number of breakthroughs in the area of personally-ingested magic. His most famous invention in this area was a yellowish-green potion which allowed humans to talk to plants.

All of these inventions were marketed by FrobozzCo International, providing Thomas Alva with generous royalties. But he spurned wealth, living in a small room behind his laboratory and sleeping on an unfinished wooden board. Thomas Alva died in 789 GUE from a severe case of splinters.

# JAM 883

| Sand Day | Mud Day | Grues Day | Wands Day | Birthday | Frob Day™ | Star Day |
|---|---|---|---|---|---|---|
| **KRAZY KWOTES** "A good lawyer is much better than a good husband." –Lucrezia Flathead | | | | 1 EATEN MOON *Dimwit's Birthday Observed* | 2 | 3 |
| 4 FAST MOON | 5 *Treaty of Znurg (474 GUE)* | 6 | 7 | 8 *Dimwit's Birthday Observed* | 9 | 10 |
| 11 | 12 | 13 | 14 *Capital moved to Flatheadia (771 GUE)* | 15 *Dimwit's Birthday Observed* | 16 | 17 |
| 18 | 19 | 20 | 21 | 22 *Dimwit's Birthday Observed* | 23 | 24 |
| 25 | 26 | 27 | 28 | 29 *Dimwit's Birthday Observed* | 30 | |

*Frob Day is a traderune of the Frobozz Magic Day Company.*

# LEONARDO FLATHEAD
## Artist and Scientist
## (731–789)

Little notice was taken of Leonardo Flathead as a child. He was shy and quiet, and quite overshadowed by his aggressive older brothers. It wasn't until his arrival at Galepath University that his genius blossomed and the world began to take notice.

While at the University, Leonardo wrote several major treatises which revolutionized scientific thought. The most famous of these disproved the hoary myth that the world sits on the back of a giant turtle, proving instead that the world actually rests on the head of an enormous troll.

After his University days were over, Leonardo turned from science to art. He became the most famous painter in the land: noblemen from every province were escorted to his studio by Dimwit's personal militia to have their portraits painted.

Unfortunately, during his later years Leonardo became quite senile, and his painting style deteriorated. He took to flinging paint at his canvasses in much the same way that a Borphee baker flings bits of dough into a hot oven to make Frobolli Cakes. His studio became caked with layer upon layer of splattered paint. It was during this period that his famous incomplete work, "Obstructed View of Fjord," was lost.

Leonardo made a final, feeble attempt to recapture his former greatness by moving into other media beside paint, but these efforts led to his tragic end. In 789, while working on a large statue intended for the harbor of Antharia, he suffered a fatal plunge into a vat of molten granola.

# JELLY 883

| Sand Day | Mud Day | Grues Day | Wands Day | Birthday | Frob Day[TR] | Star Day |
|---|---|---|---|---|---|---|
| -5 | **TID BITZ** The great Thaumaturgist, Davmar, spent six years of his life as a zucchini farmer, but was allergic to zucchinis and could not eat them himself! | | | | | 1 |
| 2 WHITE MOON | 3 *Double Fanucci became National Sport of Quendor (761 GUE)* | 4 *Filfre Day* | 5 | 6 *Dimwit's Birthday Observed* | 7 | 8 |
| 9 | 10 | 11 SUDDEN MOON | 12 | 13 *Dimwit's Birthday Observed* | 14 | 15 |
| 16 | 17 | 18 | 19 | 20 *Dimwit's Birthday Observed* | 21 | 22 |
| 23 / 30 | 24 / 31 | 25 ? *St. Quakko's Day (maybe)* | 26 | 27 *Dimwit's Birthday Observed* | 28 | 29 |

*Frob Day is a traderune of the Frobozz Magic Day Company.*

## LUCREZIA FLATHEAD

### Legendary Murderess or Innocent Widow?

### (735–789)

Of all the Twelve Flatheads, it is most difficult to separate history from legend when studying Lucrezia, the only sister to eleven aggressive brothers. Showing a total lack of understanding for her delicate position, detractors have cruelly tried to claim that Lucrezia had a warped mind.

At the tender age of sixteen, Lucrezia married a very rich but very old nobleman from Gurth, Marcus Bzart-Foodle. Ten-and-a-half months later, he died in bed with his bride. Afterward, Bzart-Foodle's doctor could not recall whether he had warned Lucrezia to avoid over-exciting her husband's weak heart.

Lucrezia's second husband, a wealthy land baron from Mareilon named Oddzoe Glorb III, was found dead just five weeks after the wedding, his body mangled by hellhounds. It was quite understandable that Lucrezia had her multi-volume hellhound training manual removed from the house at once; the sight of it must have brought back tragic memories.

Five days later, Lucrezia sought consolation in a third marriage, to the Governor of Antharia, Hirax Mumbleton. Only two days after that, Antharia was without a governor. Hirax had been discovered in his office, smothered under a ton of raw granola. His sobbing widow immediately cancelled delivery of her daily truckloads of granola, in order to avoid any similar tragedies.

After her next fifteen husbands, all wealthy lords, died on their wedding nights, royal insiders reported that she was so distraught by her tragic string of bad luck that she was becoming dangerously suicidal. Elder brother Dimwit was finally forced into action, and had her locked up in a cell in the dungeon for her own safety. She languished in that cell for the remaining fifteen years of her life. During this period, some 1,800 prison guards were mysteriously poisoned. Some legends say that her own death, in 789, was self-induced.

# AUGUR 883

| Sand Day | Mud Day | Grues Day | Wands Day | Birthday | Frob Day™ | Star Day |
|---|---|---|---|---|---|---|
| **QUICKIE QUIZ** What is the busiest seaport in the Eastlands? Answer: Port Foozle | | 1 | 2 | 3 *Dimwit's Birthday Observed* | 4 SMALL MOON | 5 |
| 6 *St. Bovus' Day* | 7 *Gnusto spell invented (769 GUE)* | 8 | 9 | 10 *Dimwit's Birthday Observed* | 11 | 12 |
| 13 | 14 | 15 dentist 1:50 | 16 *First Zorkmid minted (699 GUE)* | 17 *Dimwit's Birthday Observed* | 18 | 19 |
| 20 | 21 | 22 | 23 | 24 *Dimwit's Birthday Observed* | 25 | 26 |
| 27 | 28 LARGE MOON | 29 | 30 | 31 *Dimwit's Birthday Observed* | **FUN FAX** Bottomless pits are the second-leading cause of death in Flatheadia. | |

*Frob Day is a traderune of the Frobozz Magic Day Company.*

## RALPH WALDO FLATHEAD
### The Poet of the Empire
### (737–789)

An unspoken Flathead family motto was "quantity over quality," and no one demonstrated that tenet better than Ralph Waldo. During his 40-plus years of putting pen to parchment, he wrote 912 novels, 4,000 short stories, and an incredible 87,000 sonnets. His essays have never been successfully counted.

Ralph Waldo spent eleven years at Antharia University, collecting a chestful of degrees, including three doctorates: Doctor of Idyllic Poetry, Doctor of Excellent Elegies, and Doctor of Octameter Odes. He was very proud of his academic accomplishments, and always signed his name "Ralph Waldo Flathead, D.I.P., D.E.E., D.O.O."

Fresh out of college and flush with the enthusiasm of youth, Ralph Waldo wrote a series of lengthy essays which he hoped would uplift the human spirit. Sadly and inexplicably, these essays lifted little more than the profits of the Frobozz Magic Writing Paper Company. The essays from this period include "On the Benefits of Keeping Ears Clean" and "Why Doorknobs are Necessary." Also during this period, he wrote "On the Discoloration of Roadside Slush," but the manuscript was lost before it could be published, leaving Ralph Waldo disconsolate for years.

During his middle years, Ralph Waldo spent nearly half a decade living in the granola mines of Antharia. It was during this period that he wrote his longest work, a 60,000-verse epic about the varieties of moss that one finds in granola mines.

Toward the end of his life, Ralph Waldo specialized in exploring related themes, as brilliantly demonstrated by the four sonnets found by his deathbed:

Sonnet #87,177 "Ode to a Tiny Moist Avocado Pit"
Sonnet #87,178 "Ode to Another Tiny Moist Avocado Pit"
Sonnet #87,179 "Ode to Two Tiny Moist Avocado Pits"
Sonnet #87,180 "Ode to Two Still-Tiny-But-Less-Moist Avocado Pits"

Ralph Waldo died in 789 GUE. An autopsy revealed that the cause of death was an overdose of avocados.

# SUSPENDUR 883

| Sand Day | Mud Day | Grues Day | Wands Day | Birthday | Frob Day[TR] | Star Day |
|---|---|---|---|---|---|---|
| **FUN FAX** Some experts claim that Dimwit Flathead could access a secret wing of his castle by sitting on his favorite throne and snapping his fingers. | | | | | 1 | 2 *Time Travel Spell invented (927 GUE)* |
| 3 | 4 TWO MOONS *Leisure Day* | 5 | 6 | 7 *Dimwit's Birthday Observed* | 8 | 9 |
| 10 | 11 *Double Fanucci Championships* | 12 | 13 ONE & A HALF MOONS | 14 *Dimwit's Birthday Observed* | 15 | 16 |
| 17 | 18 | 19 | 20 | 21 *Dimwit's Birthday Observed* | 22 MISSING MOON | 23 |
| 24 | 25 | 26 WEIRD MOON | 27 | 28 *Dimwit's Birthday Observed* | 29 | 30 |

*Frob Day is a traderune of the Frobozz Magic Day Company.*

# JOHN PAUL FLATHEAD

## Seaman and Explorer

## (738–789)

All the Flathead aunts and uncles predicted early on that John Paul would find his destiny at sea. He loved boats so much that the royal carpenters were ordered to produce a flotilla of 1,400 vessels for his bathtub.*

From an early age, John Paul suffered from an inferiority complex derived from being the second "John" among the Flathead children.** This complex made John Paul determined to become a world-famous seafaring adventurer.

At sea, his feats ranged from the courageous (he was the first person to traverse the Great Sea in a one-man ship) to the curious (he set a new record for the most circumnavigations of Antharia on a raft towed by groupers).

In 766 GUE, at the age of 28, John Paul joined the royal navy; by 771, he was the ranking admiral; by 773, every ship in the navy had been sunk or lost at sea. John Paul retired shortly thereafter.

He spent his latter days touring the Flathead Ocean, collecting curios and unusual pets from all corners of the world. Among the most interesting: a large blue toad named "Otto" who was known for his extraordinary appetite and his curmudgeonly personality.

John Paul died in 789 GUE, during a vacation in Grubbo-by-the-Sea, when his old nemesis, the great white jellyfish, finally caught up with him.

*His bathtub had to be consequently enlarged; a large inland sea resulted.*

***In his autobiography, Mumberthrax explains that when he named John Paul he "simply forgot about John D."*

# OTTOBUR 883

| Sand Day | Mud Day | Grues Day | Wands Day | Birthday | Frob Day[TR] | Star Day |
|---|---|---|---|---|---|---|
| 1 | 2 FULL MOON | 3 | 4 | 5 *Dimwit's Birthday Observed* | 6 *St. Wiskus' Day* | 7 |
| 8 | 9 | 10 | 11 | 12 *Dimwit's Birthday Observed* | 13 | 14 |
| 15 FULL SUN | 16 | 17 | 18 | 19 *Dimwit's Birthday Observed* | 20 | 21 |
| 22 | 23 | 24 | 25 | 26 *Dimwit's Birthday Observed* | 27 | 28 |
| 29 | 30 | 31 | **TID BITZ** Antharian cave-dwelling witches can sometimes be summoned by coughing. | | | |

*Frob Day is a traderune of the Frobozz Magic Day Company.*

# FRANK LLOYD FLATHEAD

## Royal Architect
## (741–789)

As children, all the Flathead siblings adored playing with blocks.* However, only Frank Lloyd drew plans before building.

Frank Lloyd got his big break at the tender age of 17, when his father, King Mumberthrax, commissioned him to design a new wing for Castle Egreth. The resulting wing was breathtakingly impressive. As Frank Lloyd himself wrote, "the conjunction of space and time seems to interface in a pre-subjected instantiation of the underrepresented whole." Frank Lloyd became, overnight, the hottest architect in the Kingdom.**

His reputation established, Frank Lloyd designed virtually every important Quendorian building during his three decades as Official Court Architect. His designs ranged from his vacation chalet in the Gray Mountains to the Great Meeting Hall of the Enchanters' Guild in Borphee, but Frank Lloyd is best known for his most ambitious work: the 400-story FrobozzCo Building in Flatheadia.

Overlooking exaggerations such as "on a clear day you can see the FrobozzCo Building from anywhere in the world," it is still the most ambitious building ever designed or built. A FrobozzCo Building address is most prestigious, and Frank Lloyd himself had a penthouse office, until a slight case of acrophobia forced him to relocate to a nineteenth-story office with a pleasant southern exposure.

The carcinogenic chemicals used in the eighth century to create blueprints finally took their toll on Frank Lloyd, and he died in 789 GUE.

**Nanny Beeble, governess to the children, recalls that many had teams of slaves whose exclusive job it was to move the larger blocks.*

***The fact that the new wing of Egreth collapsed two years later, killing over 4,000 royal guests, was credited to a miscalculation on the stonemason's part. He was summarily executed.*

# MUMBERBUR 883

| Sand Day | Mud Day | Grues Day | Wands Day | Birthday | Frob Day[TR] | Star Day |
|---|---|---|---|---|---|---|
| **DID U KNOW?** Some silly people actually believe that the Empire will collapse on Curse Day this year. | | | 1 | 2 *Dimwit's Birthday Observed* | 3 NEW MOON | 4 |
| 5 | 6 | 7 | 8 | 9 *Dimwit's Birthday Observed* | 10 | 11 *Veterinarian's Day* |
| 12 leave for Flatheadia | 13 | 14 *Curse Day* | 15 | 16 NEW SUN *Dimwit's Birthday Observed* | 17 | 18 |
| 19 | 20 | 21 | 22 FULL FLAKE | 23 *Dimwit's Birthday Observed* | 24 | 25 |
| 26 | 27 RAD MOON | 28 | 29 | 30 *Dimwit's Birthday Observed* | **KRAZY KWOTES** "You ain't nothing but a hellhound." –Elvis Flathead | |

*Frob Day is a traderune of the Frobozz Magic Day Company.*

# BABE FLATHEAD
## Athletic Superstar
## (748–789)

Often called the flattest of the Flatheads, Babe, the youngest of the twelve, was born with an aptitude for sport. He demonstrated his dexterity and coordination early on, throwing baby blocks at his older siblings with impressive speed and accuracy.

As a youth, he was always captain of the Little League teams, thanks in part to pressure applied by his uncle, Mayor Fiorello Flathead. Even as a teenager, he was something of a lady's man and a party animal, and his older brother Dimwit would frequently have to bail the Babe out of jail following one infraction or another. By all accounts, Babe and Dimwit, despite their 25-year age difference, were closest of all the Flathead siblings.

When he reached college age, Babe selected Mithicus Province University from amongst many eager suitors. At MPU, Babe was a 43-letter man, leading his team to championships in every existing college sport and several non-existent ones as well.*

Throughout the Babe's professional sports career, he excelled in everything he tried: bocce, tag-team kayaking, full-court furbish. There was only one exception. Try as he might, Babe could not master Double Fanucci. Even the unexplained disappearances of the 339 leading Double Fanucci players failed to get Babe into the championships. Fanucci experts believe that Babe's difficulty with the game could be traced to one weakness: his failure to remember that three undertrumps after an opponent's discard of a Trebled Fromp is an indefensible gambit.

By 782 GUE, the Babe was such a phenomenal drawing card that Dimwit constructed the kingdom's largest sporting arena, Flathead Stadium, in his honor. It was there, during the shark-wrestling semi-finals in 789 GUE, that the youngest of the Twelve Flatheads met his end.

**Many experts feel that Babe's teams would have won these championships even if every competing school had NOT had their QCAA memberships revoked.*

# DISMEMBUR 883

| Sand Day | Mud Day | Grues Day | Wands Day | Birthday | Frob Day[TR] | Star Day |
|---|---|---|---|---|---|---|
| **QUICKIE QUIZ** Who said "A home that's cut in half usually falls over"? Answer: Abraham Flathead | | | | | 1 | 2 |
| 3 | 4 SEMI-FLAKE | 5 BULL MOON | 6 | 7 *Dimwit's Birthday Observed* | 8 | 9 *Unnatural Acts (672 GUE)* |
| 10 | 11 | 12 | 13 HAPPY MOON | 14 *Dimwit's Birthday Observed* | 15 | 16 DARK FLAKE |
| 17 | 18 | 19 | 20 | 21 BLUE MOON *Dimwit's Birthday Observed* | 22 | 23 |
| 24 / 31 *Beginning of Flathead Dynasty (659 GUE)* | 25 | 26 HALF-BOZ SUN | 27 | 28 *Dimwit's Birthday Observed* | 29 GRUE MOON | 30 ZIKKO FLAKE |

*Frob Day is a traderune of the Frobozz Magic Day Company.*

# Enchanter

Welcome to the world of the Enchanter saga — a world where magic is commonplace, a world where guilds of professional magic-users spend their lifetimes mastering the intracacies of thaumaturgy, a world where great forces of evil must constantly be held at bay
An evil Warlock has subjugated the land to his power. All who have opposed him have failed. But many years ago, in another age, the great Elders of the Circle of Enchanters foresaw the possibility of these dreaded occurrences. They realized that no fully accomplished Enchanter could penetrate the Warlock's defenses unrecognized, and knew that the task of freeing the land would fall to a journeyman conjurer. You have been identified as the Apprentice Enchanter who must save the land from the Warlock. As a fledgling Enchanter, you have learned your lessons but have not faced all your tests. You possess great power, but in the ranks of necromancers you are a lowly and ignorant person indeed. You have been well trained in the basics of magic, and you will be greatly aided by the spells you know and the spells you will learn. But you must also rely on your powers of observation and quick wits.

About the Author
Marc Blank. A graduate of MIT and the Albert Einstein College of Medicine, Marc has been involved in writing interactive fiction since its formative period in the late 1970s. Co-author of the original mainframe version of ZORK in 1977, he was instrumental in laying the groundwork for the appearance of interactive fiction on personal computers in the early 1980s. He is co-author of ZORK I, ZORK II, ZORK II, and ENCHNATER, and is sole author of DEADLINE, the first interactive mystery. His continuing work in interactive technologies in large part made Infocom's name synonymous with interactive fiction. His mother still wishes he would practice medicine.
Dave Lebling was born in Washington, D. C. and grew up in suburban Maryland. He attended the Massachusetts Institute of Technology, and worked at MIT's Laboratory for Computer Science, where he developed an interest in computer entertainments. He was a co-author of the original mainframe ZORK. He has co-authored ZORK I, ZORK II, ZORK III, and ENCHANTER, and written STARCROSS and SUSPECT on his own.

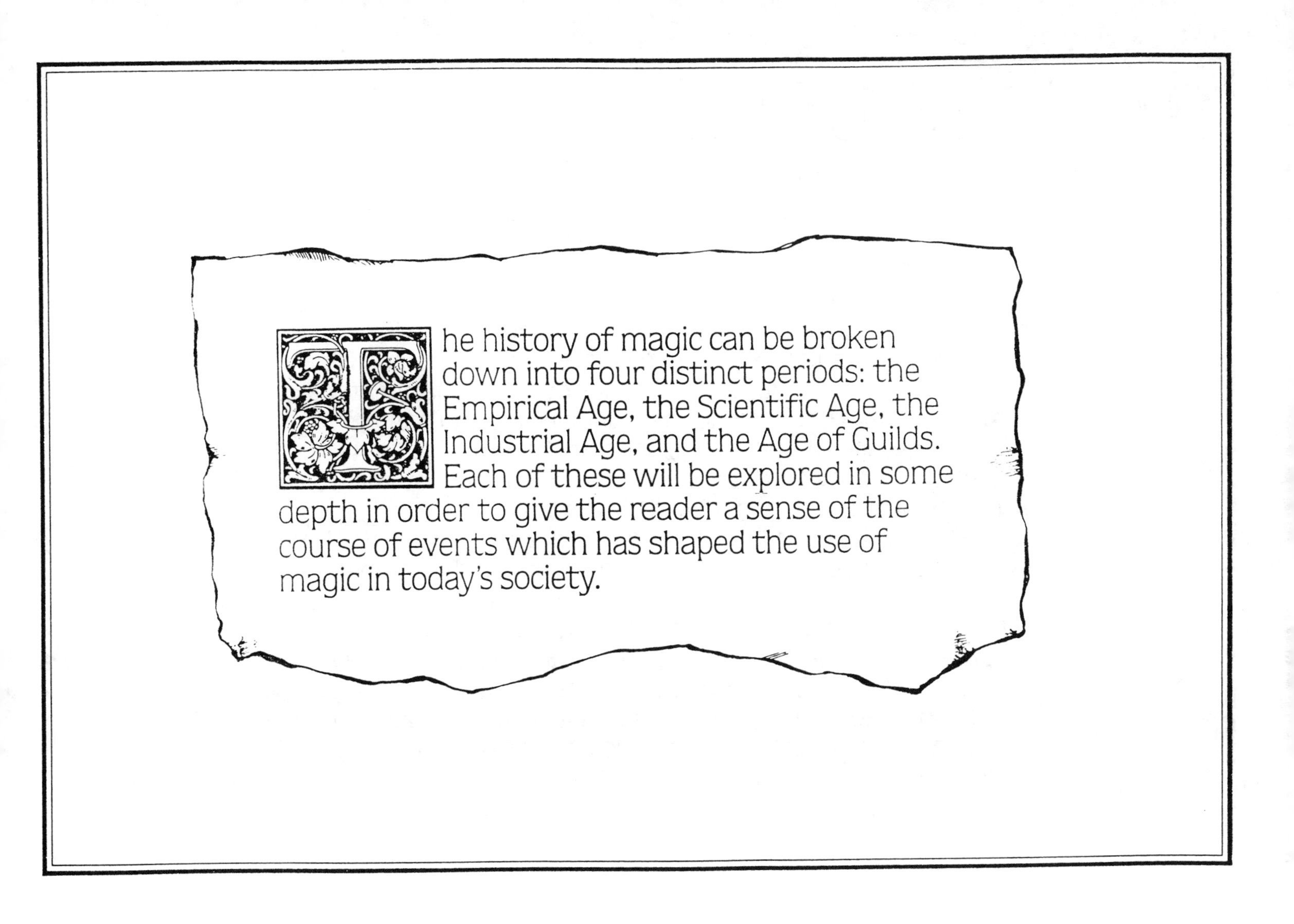

The history of magic can be broken down into four distinct periods: the Empirical Age, the Scientific Age, the Industrial Age, and the Age of Guilds. Each of these will be explored in some depth in order to give the reader a sense of the course of events which has shaped the use of magic in today's society.

# The Empirical Age

Primitive cultures had naturally assumed that the disorderly nature of our world was due to such supernatural causes as magic. With the founding of the "natural" sciences, however, nature was increasingly viewed as being orderly. As the sciences progressed, the knowledge and lore of magic largely disappeared. As early as the 5th century GUE (Great Underground Empire), however, such students of the mystic arts as Bizboz and Dinbar thoroughly examined ancient writings on the subject. Bizboz himself wrote what became the seminal work in Thaumaturgy, "On the Presence of Incredibly Weird Stuff Going On," in 473 GUE, in which he claimed to have discovered "for-the-most-part Natural Rules" by which this "Weird Stuff" is ordered.

This work was ridiculed by the leading scholars of the time, leading to Bizboz's removal from the faculty at the Galepath University, and, eventually, to his tragic suicide in 475 GUE. His work, however, encouraged others in the pursuit of magical knowledge, with mixed results. Charlatans, claiming to have created magical potions and powders, regularly fooled the gullible population into buying potions which claimed to do such things as "reverse hair loss" and "draw Trebled Fromps in Double Fanucci." Such appeals to public ignorance led King Duncanthrax in 672 GUE to write the Unnatural Acts, which provided stiff penalties for those convicted of selling "Unnatural or Supernatural substances."

## Scientific Age

While the charlatans were at work, serious students took up the cause of magic, attempting to explain the natural world as a by-product of the interrelated workings of the sciences of Physics, Medicine, Chemistry, Mathematics, and Thaumaturgy. Their success in demonstrating the so-called first principles of Thaumaturgy, namely Presence, Incantation, and Unusual Effect, led to a loosening of the Unnatural Acts to allow what became known as Scientific Thaumaturgy. During this period, the first chapter of the Guild of Enchanters was founded at the tiny hamlet of Accardi-by-the-Sea by the great thaumaturge, Vilboz.

During the reign of Frobwit the Flatter (701–727 GUE), the art and science of Thaumaturgy flourished. The first reliable Incantation Device, known to scholars as the Hyperbolic Incantation Concentrator, was produced at the Thaumaturgical Institute in 723 GUE. The long, thin, portable device, nicknamed the "magic wand" by the lay press, became an instant sensation among the populace, and gained a certain measure of respect for the fledgling science.

A major advance in Thaumaturgy occurred when Davmar, working in newly-crowned King Mumberthrax Flathead's laboratory, discovered a means by which Incantation could be stored on special Presence-imbued paper. These so-called scrolls were found, however, to be destroyed during the spells' Incantation. Nonetheless, scrolls soon replaced the temperamental and poorly-understood "wand" as the primary means of Incantation.

The problem of imbuing Presence became a deterrent to the rapid growth of magical science. The creation of a single powerful scroll could take literally months for even the most creative and productive thaumaturge. This roadblock prevented the widespread use of magic for generations.

# Industrial Age

The Industrial Age dawned in 769 GUE with a discovery by a little-known thaumaturge named Berzio. Berzio, working for years in his own self-made workshop and often going for days without food, drink, or sleep, created the means by which Presence could be transferred from a scroll to a specially impregnated paper by use of a simple spell, which he named after his dog, Gnusto. This paper, in turn, held the Presence even after the Incantation had been finished, solving the major problem in spell production. The euphoria which greeted this discovery was tempered by the finding that very powerful spells could not be transferred in this way. Nevertheless, spell "books," which were capable of holding dozens of spells, were produced in great number, leading to the founding of a new industry.

Another advance in Thaumaturgy occurred with the finding that certain liquids and powders could be imbued with the magical Presence. Such potions are of great interest, although their limitations have prevented them from supplanting scrolls as the primary method of Incantation. The first of these potions, which obviates the need for food and drink, was given the name BERZIO, in honor of the great thaumaturge.

# Age of Guilds

As the use of magic became more prevalent, so did the problems inherent in its use. Since magic had become available to people in all professions, conflicts arose. One famous issue involved the question of whether the plumber's FIZMO spell ("cause stopped-up pipes to unclog") could be sold as a digestive aid by physicians. The issue came to a head in the aftermath of the Endless Fire of 773 GUE, so named because it burned for 4 weeks after destroying the city of Mareilon. It was later found to have been started by a civil servant who thought he was casting the ZEMDOR spell ("turn original into triplicate") but who, instead, cast the ZIMBOR spell ("turn one really big city into lots of tiny, little ashes").

This led Lord Dimwit Flathead (the Excessive) to issue a series of 5,521 edicts over the following few weeks, which had the effect of severely limiting access to magic (and, incidentally, lawyers). Henceforth, all magic was entrusted to the various Guilds of Enchanters, which by now existed in many small communities. Each Guild, whose elders comprised the so-called Circle of Enchanters, was empowered to form schools for the training of new Enchanters. This official sanctioning of the Guilds led to the formation of numerous other chapters, with membership in the various Guilds in excess of 2,000 by the year 800 GUE. Despite the fall of the Great Underground Empire in 883 GUE under the feeble-minded reign of Wurb Flathead, the Guild of Enchanters remains virtually unchanged in character today.

# Today's Enchanter

Since the fall of the Empire, magic has again become a mysterious art, practiced primarily by trained Sorcerers, although a few spells, such as UMBOZ ("obviate need for dusting") and NERZO ("balance checkbook"), have been approved for over-the-counter sale. Upon graduation from an accredited Thaumaturgical College, an Enchanter is given a spell book with a few spells, none of which has great power. As an Enchanter continues his or her studies, new spells may be obtained; these may be copied into a spell book for use whenever the occasion warrants.

The Enchanter's job is not as easy as is commonly thought. An Enchanter must memorize a spell written in a spell book before casting it. (Spells on scrolls and those which have been permanently etched in the memory by training needn't be memorized.) Moreover, if an Enchanter needs to use a particular spell twice, it must be memorized twice, since the effort of casting it makes it a jumble in one's memory. In fact, even a night's sleep will make an Enchanter forget any memorized spells. But, in spite of the rigors of spell casting, the personal rewards are great, and the job of Enchanter remains a popular and well-respected vocation.

# An Afterthought

The most fitting words regarding the history of magic were written over a century ago by the renowned historian Ozmar in 821 GUE. He wrote: "The greatest irony is this: that the ancients of our kind were nearer to knowing the truth about Science than those who called themselves Scientists. Science has taught us much and given us new words for old mysteries. But beneath these words are mysteries, and beneath them more mysteries. The pursuit of Magic has given these mysteries meaning and provided for our people great benefits unrealized as yet by Science. One day, perhaps, a great union will be formed between Magic and Science, and the final mysteries will be solved."

:If you truly are the one
brave enough to face
unspeakable peril ·
let your wizardly
powers reveal
our words ·

Hear us...

We, the Circle of Enchanters, have foreseen that a ruthless and powerful Evil may one day seize this land. Should that time arrive, we also foresee the coming of age of a young Enchanter, one whose heart and wits may triumph over the Warlock's dark necromancy. It is our hope that this Enchanter hears our words.

We cannot see your face through the mists of time, but this we know in truth... You are promising in magic but have not gained your full skills. That is as it must be, for the Warlock would recognize one of the Council of Elders and would sense the presence of a more powerful Enchanter. Thus, in your obscurity you may find your way to his lair before he knows the mortal danger you pose.

Four spells will arm you as you begin your quest. FROTZ shall turn darkness to light. NITFOL shall build a bridge of language to all the animals of the land. GNUSTO writes magic; by it you shall commit spells to your treasured spell book. BLORB is a spell of protection; with it you may guard your most precious possession.

·Never forget, young Enchanter, that magic is your only weapon. By your vows to the Council of Elders you have cast aside the common protections of sword and armor. Therefore you will need many more spells to accomplish your quest. These will be revealed to you. Always be alert.

Though your way will be harsh and your steps fraught with danger, remember throughout your quest that you are the only hope of this land. We pray that our successors will choose wisely and that you will prove yourself worthy of the title Enchanter.

Signed with our mark and cast into the ages...

The Circle of Enchanters

# Sorcerer

Welcome to the world of the Enchanter saga — a world where magic is commonplace, a world where guilds of professional magic-users spend their lifetimes mastering the intracacies of thaumaturgy, a world where great forces of evil must constantly be held at bay.

In your late youth you left home to join the Guild of Enchanters. After years of schooling, you achieved the rank of Apprentice Enchanter. In fulfillment of an ancient prophecy, you were sent to find Krill, an evil warlock who had loosed a pestilence upon the land, and who threatened the very existence of the Circle of Enchanters. Only someone guileless and inexperienced in the ways of magic could slip into Krill's realm unnoticed. By defeating Krill, you earned a seat on the Circle of Enchanters, sitting at the right hand of your mentor, the leader of the Guild, Belboz the Necromancer. Several years have passed, and you have grown very close to Belboz as you studied under his tutelage, learning the ways of magic from one of the world's most learned practitioners. But lately, Belboz has seemed troubled, preoccupied, withdrawn ... small things only a friend would notice. You have even heard frightening noises coming from his chamber, and the voices of conversation when Belboz was supposedly alone. His temper has seemed short the last few days, and the look in his eyes sends cold shivers down your back. Could some evil spirit be at work here? You are sleepless from worry — Belboz is possibly the most powerful Enchanter in the kingdom. If his powers were used by the forces of darkness instead of the forces of light, who knows what would result? And now, unbeknownst to you, Belboz has vanished.

About the Author

Steve Meretzky was born in mid-1957, frightening the Soviet Union into the early launching of its Sputnik satellite. Meretzky's gestalt was shaped by a number of painful childhood experiences, including rooting for the New York Mets. He blames his interactive fiction on a combination of growing up in Yonkers and studying at MIT. (We use "studying" in the most general sense.) Meretzky has never been a rutabaga farmer, and believes that eating granola is a decision that should be left to the individual's conscience. Meretzky now lives near Boston. He apologizes for PLANETFALL and SORCERER, but refuses to take full responsibility for THE HITCHHIKER'S GUIDE TO THE GALAXY.

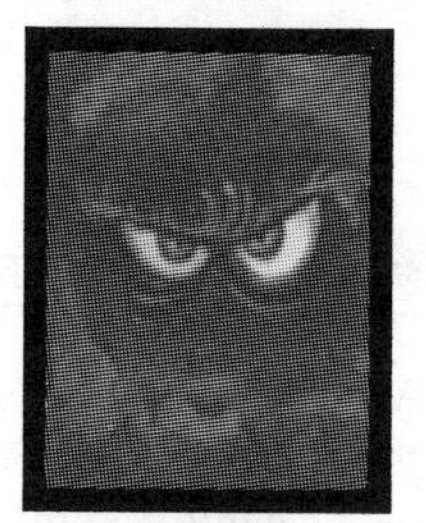

**GRUE**

A Sinister, lurking presence in the dark places of the earth. Favorite snack is unwary Enchanters. Fears light: No grue has ever been seen by the light of day. Toxicologists believe that grues are probably black - black - red - black - purple.

**DORN**

Can paralyze with a single glare from its powerful eyes (range: roughly 3' for young beasts to 20' for adults). Dorns commonly inhabit crags and shadows near cliff bases. According to the last words of dying explorers, dorn beasts are gray - purple - black - gray - white.

**NABIZ**

A nabiz is mostly mouth, that is mostly teeth. Instinctively attacks enemy's weak point. Contrary to folklore, cannot fly, but leaps vast distances. Is repulsed by the color blue; hence that color's popularity in adventurer's grab. Nabiz are purple - black - black - black - red.

**SURMIN**

Characterized by malodorous breath, lice ridden fur, and general repulsiveness. If allowed to approach close enough, can bore its victim to death by reciting Greater Borphee County Penal Codes. A newly-shaved surmin is black - black - purple - red - black.

**KOBOLD**

Lives in small tribes in caverns and very dark forests. Similar to paskald, except middle toe is shorter than toes that flank it; also, far more belligerent. If attacked, will fight back; if not attacked, will fight back anyway. Coloration: red - purple - black - purple - red.

**YIPPLE**

Master of disguise, able to change form. In the wild, may bite if disturbed. Violently allergic to many kinds of animal wastes. Tame yipples make wonderful pets, but should be kept out of cookie jar when guests visit. On a white background, yipples look gray - purple - white - purple - black.

## INFOTATER

**ROTGRUB**

Less than 1" long; smells like very cheap old cheese; impervious to all forms of magic. Hides in food until ingested, then burrows straight to victim's brain and feeds for years before death mercifully arrives. Common household rotgrubs are gray - red - grey - purple - red.

**BLOODWORM**

Found in shallow underground pools; often mistaken for mossy boulders. Pointy, retractable fangs can extend up to 32". Most bloodworms are repelled by the smell of boiled chives. Bloodworms are usually white - gray - black - red - black

**DRYAD**

Also called "tree sprite." Beautifully shy. Many spend lifetime under one tree. If coaxed, may reveal location of forest treasures. Will fight only in self-defense and only in large numbers, pelting foes with tons of rose petals. When awake, dryads are black - gray - white - red - red.

**HELLHOUND**

Fast, Fierce, and capable of devouring a human 12 times its size in 3.5 seconds. Normally inhabits burnt-out or enchanted woods and rarely ventures beyond it own turf, even in pursuit of prey. Hellhounds are purple - white - grey - red - grey.

**ORC**

Erstwhile warring race who became civilized through their fondness for computer adventure games. Although a small faction (Hi-res Orcs) enjoy graphics adventures, the vast majority (Orcs of Zork) prefer text games. By the light of CRT screen, orcs are red - gray - purple - gray - red.

**BROGMOID**

In rare cases, these squat creatures can achieve intelligence level of a 3-year old human. Often seen in wild foraging in huge packs for edible rocks. Live much longer in captivity; can even be trained to perform simple tasks. Usually red - purple - red - black - purple.

## INFOTATER

# Gazing Into the Orb

LETTERS TO THE EDITOR

To the editor: In your otherwise excellent article on the FILFIRE spell, you neglected to mention its derivation. FILFRE is a modification of the expression "Feel Free," which perhaps explains its unrestrained use among some Enchanters.

P.D.L., Borphee

To the editor: So Orkan of Thriff is now selling wand racks? He's a Guildmaster, not a carpenter! Next thing you know, actors will be selling salad dressing.

H.D.A.,Accardi

To the editor: I'm sure many of your readers would be suprised to learn that there are some remote areas of the Empire where people still do not practice magic. An article about these under-developed communities would be quite amusing.

S.W.G.,Mithicus

To the editor: Your recent article entitled "Should Enchanters in Glass Mazes Throw Stones?" reminded me of a few other age-old questions that perhaps modern magic can answer: Which came first, the time paradox or the tamed parrot Awkes? Is a zorkmid truly the root of boll weevils? If the land were the sky and the sky were the land, would things fall up and grow down?

S.E.M.Whereabouts Unknown

# SPECIAL BOOK EXCERPT:
# *"Spells and the Single Sorcerer"*

**by Wilbar Memboob**

*[This is the second of three excerpts to appear in POPULAR ENCHANTING magazine. Last month's installment dismissed many of the myths surrounding single Sorcerers, among them the common notion that single Sorcerers like granola. This month's installment is adapted from chapter "friendship...and More," and discusses the importance of making a good first impression. The final excerpt, discussing such practical matters as spells for single-serving potions and Aolitaire Fanuccii, will appear next month. Wilbar Memboob is the author of "The Joy of Spells" and "The Enchanter Never Rings Twice: 101 Uses for REZROV."]*

Many otherwise fine and distinguished Sorcerers are shy or ugly, or, generally, both. This does not mean, however, that they must lead a solitary existence or abstain from the simple ;pleasures of courtship. Several thaumaturgical suppliers sell a WIDE assortment of self-improvement spells and potions, and unless you are "dobold ugly," most will work with few or no unpleasant side effects.

It is impossible to predict when a particular self-improvement spell or potion will be needed (unless one is a very, very good Sorcerer). carrying a six-pack of assorted potions can therefore save a situation. For instance, suppose you were walking beside a field of blossoming dragondilsm and you met an attractive person of the opposite sex. would this person remark "Aren't the dragondils lovely," you might reply: "Oh, is that what they are?" or simply "Yes." or, worse, "I've seen nicer." But if you had in your possession the SIRANO potion, you might surreptitiously quaff it and reply :
"As lovely and golden as the rain-washed air is clear and sparkling, and fragrant and fresh as you eyes are poetic and inspiring." You must of course realize that you get what you pay for. Some so-called "discount" or "bargain" potions are no bargain at all. A SIRANO potion that wears off mid-sentence can be disastrous, as you're likely to say the first thing that comes to your mind, which is bound to be ridiculous: "Your lips are like rubies, your eyes like alabaster, your hands like...like poached rotgrub."

Once you have captured your new acquaintance's attention with a charming or witty remark, you must act fast! Many Sorcerers cast the FAIFT spell ("change appearance to look younger" ) on themselves. This is generally a mistake. If your face is reminiscent of a frog, you will suddenly look like a tadpole; if you're overweight, you may become a piglet. A better strategy is to cast the IMALI spell ("worsen eyesight") on your friend. The spell is painless and temporary, and should your dupe comment upon blurry vision, you might remember ELVIS Flathead's hit "LOVE IS BLIND," and suggest that your kind-hearted spell in fact prevented total blindness.

Before I am accused of condoning deceit as the basis for a relationship, let me state outright that the casting of spells - on yourself or on your partner - is permissible only for the first few days of a relationship. If you cannot keep your acquaintance's interest without magic, then you should let go and part ways. Particularly reprehensible are reports of Sorcerers casting body-deforming spells like BAYALA and MUSDEX on an unwilling partner to satisfy a personal preference.

NOW!

A RESURRECTION SPELL FOR EVEN THE MOST INEXPERIENCED MAGIC CASTER!

GASPAR™

From the company that developed BLORB and QUELBO comes the world's first gnustoable resurrection spell.* A breakthrough in magic technology so impressive that only the wizards at United Thaumaturgy could have done it. Look for Gaspar soon at spell scroll distributors in your town.

UNITED THAUMATURGY

"Spells and a whole lot more."

*OZMOO, by merely circumventing death, is not considered to be a true resurrection spell.

**MAKE REALLY BIG ZORKMIDS! LEARN MAGIC IN JUST 12 WEEKS!**

Our proven "Learn-at-Home" course lets you study at your own pace. Why spend your life as a woodcutter when magic can open doors for you? Over 70% of our graduates find careers in magic-related guilds. Write:

**GUE TECH,**

Borphee, Land of Frobozz
for full-color catalog.

Orkan the Enchanter, Mentor of the Thriff Chapter, says: "I wouldn't go anywhere without my CHEVAUX!" There are Spell Books – then there are CHEVAUX! Only the finest Mithican leather binding... ample pages of gnusto-receptive paper...able to withstand long study and heated battles. PLUS, the renowned CHEVAUX personalized monogram – the symbol of the discriminating Enchanter.

Order from: Priggin, Master Bookbinder and authorized CHEVAUX dealer, Miznia.

# BELBOZ AT 200:
## *Is Retirement in his Future?*

Recently, Belboz the Necromancer was lecturing to a senior class at G.U.E. Tech's School of Enchantment in Greater Borphee. The great thaumaturge departed from his prepared text on "The Baffling Behavior of Babbling Baby Brogmoids Biting Broccoli" to discuss Enchanter's Ethics, a hot issue in magical circles these days, and he gave a predictably level-headed perspective.

"What are the criteria for determining which actions are morally right and morally wrong? The most famous answer is that power and might are never wrong. But can beauty, happiness, or fireworks be ignored? Certainly not. Doing the decent thing in the face of many juicy and despicable alternatives takes enormous willpower and always arouses the skepticism of others. And an orator who sprinkles a speech with flowery and vivid images to keep his audience glued to their seats is no more ethical than a Sorcerer who casts the FOBLUB spell to achieve the same ends."

Leaders espousing moderation or temperance are rarely heard or heeded at our universities in these dreary times, yet Belboz received a 30-minute sitting ovation from his audience. (Belboz had in fact used the FOBLUB spell on the audience, gluing them to their seats.) Such is the respect and esteem accorded to this wise, crinkly-eyed master Sorcerer, who turns 200 years of age this month.

Belboz is will-know as a model Sorcerer, an exemplar for all young Enchanters. Born an orphan near Aragain Falls in the Frigid River Valley, he was the eldest of six brothers and sisters. His guardian uncle, a well-to-do but simple-minded cave digger, tried to get young Belboz interested in construction work, but Belboz talked only about magic, reading everything he could find on the subject. His uncle finally relented and sent Belboz to Borphee Harbor, where he was tutored by a master, magician for the next 20 years. ("My uncle thought thaumaturgy was a communicable fish disease, and fancied I sat on a dock for 20 years telling carp to open wide and say 'ah,'" says Belboz.) He then spent a 30-year apprenticeship in the Accardi Chapter of the Guild of Enchanters, became a full-fledged Enchanter in 820 GUE, and traveled south to Gurth and Mithicus, where he pioneered research on anti-caking additives to magic potions. His success in perfecting dozens of spells, notably the LOBAL spell ("sharpen hearing") and the CONBAK spell ("build strong bodies 12 different ways") brought him interprovincial fame and heralded his advancement to sorcerer after a mere 25 years. Unlike his peers, Belboz criticized the decadence of the royal family and foretold the collapse of the Great Underground Empire. Most fellow Sorcerers thought Belboz's warnings were shrill or foolish, but when the Empire did collapse in 883, Belboz said "I told you so." Belboz then returned to Accardi where, in 910, at the age of 153, he became Guildmaster of the Accardi Chapter. Perhaps his greatest success--certainly his most publicized--came in 952, when he destroyed the evil giant Amathradonis. Later that year he became the kingdomwide Secretary of the Guild of Enchanters, a post which he has held now for two terms.

With a life expectancy of 175 years, almost three times that of a layperson, most Sorcerers retire from the Guild and become Magicians Emeritus or Conjuration Consultants long before they become bicentenarians. At 200, Belboz is the oldest member of the Circle of Enchanters, and is the oldest guildmaster ever. Speculation is rampant, then, whether the master Sorcerer has any plans to retire.

"We-l-l-l-l," the necromancer pondered last week during an interview with POPULAR ENCHANTING, "I would like to travel. I haven't crossed the Flathead Ocean for over a century. I'd also be interested in visiting more chapters of the Guild; our flummox in [see the editorial on page 2] clearly shows we need to get our house in order. And certainly I'd like to be able to do more fishing. But I am, really, just approaching my prime. Even though I am old, my strengths and powers are at their peak."

Ask whether he thought his age impeded his work, Belboz chuckled, "All Enchanters have youth-casting spells, of course, which accounts for our longevity. I have naturally improved upon these. But I've seen some 100-year-old Enchanters who think older than I do, and therefore they are older than I am. A youth-casting spell affects the body but not the mind. It is worthless if its subject has on old mind."

"Leadership stagnation" is a term that has been bandied about lately by a number of junior Sorcerers, who feel that the lifetime appointment of Guildmasters is too long. "Guildmasters are like king, only worse," says a Sorcerer who requests anonymity. "A chapter dangles the Guildmaster post before its members like bait, enticing them to dedicate their life's work and devotion for it. A chapter selects a new Guildmaster only once in 30, 40, even 50 years. All the qualified Sorcerers who don't get chosen adopt a negative attitude knowing they;ll be Guildmasters." This negative attitude, some say is passed on to Enchanters, who pass it on to apprentices, like some communicable fish disease. While no one mentions Belboz's name specifically, his 47-year tenure as Guildmaster is an obvious target of such complaints.

"I disagree completely with the idea that we dangle the Guild master's post like bait, and it's simply not true that all other qualified Sorcerers adopt a negative attitude," says Belboz. "I agree there may be some advantages to limiting the term of a Guildmaster. But I am most upset that a Sorcerer would take offense at not being chosen Guildmaster. A

Sorcerer should be above such lowly, jealous, and power-hungry thoughts, and anyone who thinks them deserves to be turned into a newt."

So fear not, Belboz fans: The great necromancer is not ready to quit. "Ask me about my retirement again," Belboz told us, "when I turn 300."

Wanted: Need one (1) KULCAD spell scroll; will pay top dollar. Used mine foolishly; won't make same mistake. Box F4.

Wanted: Enchanter for minor Cyclops eradication work, 2 to 4 days per month. Experience desirable. Box S4.

Wanted: Letters, reminiscences, etc., by or about the thaumaturge Berzio, who invented the GNUSTO spell; for biography by noted scholar and Frobber. Box T6.

For sale: Rubber spell scrolls, rubber magic wands, rubber spell books, rubber avocados, and more! Great for gags! Largest selection of rubber products anywhere! Write for free catalog (must be over 54 years of age). Box Q5.

Personal: Dull, irritating Enchanter (M) seeks exciting, loving F for magic moments and possible lasting relationship. Must be truthful and kind, or good liar. No pros or adventurers need reply. Box Y3.

Personal: Shy, outgoing Enchanter (F) seeks lively, quiet Enchanter (M) to share the pleasures of smokeless fires. Must enjoy sadness. Box K9.

Lost: CLEESH spell scroll. Dropped while frog-watching in swamp. Small reward. Box I36.

Lost: Useless brass lantern. Has great sentimental value. Dropped long ago, far away. Would appreciate information leading to its return. Box Z1.

**Don't Be Stuck Shorthanded!**

**NYMPH-O-MANIA**

**—Temporary Nymph Services—**

- Nymphs available by the hour, by the day, by the week!
- We use exclusively the most polite and well-bred nymphs!
- Warning nymphs, guard nymphs, and serving nymphs our specialty!

—NYMPH-O-MANIA outlets are located throughout the kingdom—

***Visit one today!***

# NATE'S DISCOUNT SCROLL HOUSE

| POTIONS | LIST | NATE'S |
|---|---|---|
| BERZIO | zm4 | zm2 |
| IGNATZ | zm4 | zm3 |
| VILSTU | zm4 | zm3 |
| ONBIT | zm4 | zm3 |
| KWIN | zm4 | zm3 |
| WALDOE | zm4 | zm3 |
| KNALB | zm6 | zm4 |
| BLORT | zm12 | zm10 |

| SCROLLS | LIST | NATE'S |
|---|---|---|
| FROTZ | zm12 | zm8 |
| REZROV | zm12 | zm9 |
| BLORB | zm16 | zm12 |
| NITFOL | zm16 | zm14 |
| QUELBO | zm19 | zm15 |
| GRIGPO | zm26 | zm20 |
| YOMIN | zm28 | zm22 |
| ONKIK | zm38 | zm31 |
| YIMFIL | zm46 | zm36 |
| VEZZA | zm90 | zm74 |

| SPECIALS | LIST | NATE'S |
|---|---|---|
| MAGIC AMULETS | zm120 | zm99 |
| WANDS: *BII | zm88 | zm80 |
| *UT | zm72 | zm61 |
| *SS | zm29 | zm12 |
| SCROLL RACK | | |
| *72 | zm12 | zm4 |
| *144 | zm18 | zm6 |
| WAND RACK | | |
| *6 | zm12 | zm2 |

# Spellbreaker

Welcome to the world of the Enchanter saga — a world founded on magic, where guilds of magicians have mastered the powers of sorcery; a world now threatened with destruction. You distinguished yourself among the young Enchanters by defeating the evil warlock Krill, whose attempt to subjugate the land was thwarted by your cleverness, as your inexperience allowed you to succeed where others might have failed. This earned you a place on the Circle of Enchanters, second only to the great Belboz the Necromancer. Then Belboz himself was nearly destroyed, and your rescue of him from the evil demon Jeearr earned you the ultimate honor given a mage, the leadership of the Circle of Enchanters. Now, a crisis has befallen the kingdom. Magic itself seems to be failing. Spells fail to work or go strangely awry, the populace is confused and restive, and even the Enchanters Guild is baffled. A great conclave of the Guildmasters is ordained, and it is at this conclave that the final conflict between good and evil begins to unfold.

About the Author
Dave Lebling was born in Washington, D. C. and grew up in suburban Maryland. He attended the Massachusetts Institute of Technology, and worked at MIT's Laboratory for Computer Science, where he developed an interest in computer entertainments. He was a co-author of the original mainframe Zork. He has co-authored Zork I, Zork II, Zork III, and Enchanter, and written Starcross and Suspect on his own

DIMITHIO
OF BORPHEE
"Magic doesn't have to be great to be useful, nor does magic have to be useful to be great."
Studied under Yooman, the Musician Mage
Animal lover (adapted nitfol spell for egg-laying mammals)
Tremendously well read and good natured
Greatest skill: fireworks displays
Despised by Holnac the Cynic
Double Fanucci handicap: 127
GUSTAR
WOOMAX
"If history can teach us the difference between good and bad magic, it can teach us anything."
Author of "A Brief History of Magic," "Bizboz at Galepath," "Mage versus Archmage," "Revenge of the Dornbeasts," "The Granola Riots" (co-authored by Wilbar Memboob), and "The Coconut of Quendor: Reality or Illusion?"
Born in Greater Borphee, 880
Attended G.U.E. Tech, 907–911
Favorite author: Bizboz
Greatest skill: none known
Double Fanucci handicap: 620
BARSAP
"The hardest trick is making it look easy."
First performed before royalty, 850
Appointed Royal Magician, 875
Greatest skills: juggling, creative accounting
Guild membership revoked for dues evasion, 960
Last book read: "Magic with Mirrors"
Double Fanucci handicap: 19

## BARBEL OF GURTH

*"When I was a boy, I was told that any Enchanter could become a Guildmaster. Now I'm beginning to believe it."*

- Son of Delbor, advisor to Lord Dimwit Flathead
- Inventor of the golmac spell
- Guildmaster of Gurth City chapter since 933
- President of GAC (Gurth Arbiters Congress)
- Greatest skills: arbitrating, speaking in tongues
- Responsible for restoration of high enchantment dues
- Double Fanucci handicap: 42

## FORBURN THE WILY

*"The Encyclopedia Frobozzica calls Double Fanucci a 'game played with cards.' I don't play games; I don't play anything."*

- Never formally studied magic
- First won a spell book from an unsuspecting G.U.E. Tech student in a 902 Fanucci match
- Raised the level of play in Double Fanucci championships
- Brought new meaning to the word "chiseler"
- Greatest skill: drawing Trebled Fromps
- Double Fanucci handicap: 0.01

## BERKNIP

*"No one weeps for a necromancer."*

- Survived by 7 children and 39 grandchildren in 750 G.U.E. (he has since out-relived them)
- Greatest skill: assisting historical biographers
- Hobby: antiques (making and collecting)
- Inexplicably afraid of swords and powdered milk
- Vegetarian (adapted nitfol spell for raw oysters and crispy whole fish)
- Double Fanucci handicap: unmeasurable

FALL 966

# Frobozz Magic
# Magic Equipment Catalog

A SUBSIDIARY OF FROBOZZCO INTERNATIONAL

SPECIAL CRISIS EDITION

## NO MORE STICKY SPELL RESIDUE WITH OUR REJECTRON-COATED CAULDRONS.

Made of 100% metal, these cauldrons are perfect for mixing, brewing, and bubbling any broth or potion. A wide mouth makes stirring easy, and the broad base distributes heat slowly and evenly. Tip-proof construction, heavy-duty handles, a tight lid, and carved spout make these the finest kettles at any price.

**Available in three sizes: 20 fb, 50 fb, and 100 fb.**

20 fb . . . . . . . . . . . . . . . . . . . . . . . . . zm10
50 fb . . . . . . . . . . . . . . . . . . . . . . . . zm28
100 fb. . . . . . . . . . . . . . . . . . . . . . zm36
Set of 3. . . . . . . . . . . . . . . . . . . zm60

## PUT ON THE POWER WHEN YOU NEED IT MOST.

When you get the urge to surge, Frobozz Magic Magic Equipment rings are your best bet. Attractive and lightweight, these rings are appropriate for work or play—even Double Fanucci games! And best of all, built-in muffler lets you completely conceal the flow of magic, no matter how noisy. Ring guard prevents accidental zapping. Choose from a variety of totemic animals. To ensure correct size, please enclose any ring which is safe for transport.

**Please specify design**

Magic ring . . . . . . . . . . . . . . . . . . . . . . . . . . . . . . zm27
Deluxe model. . . . . . . . . . . . . . . . . . . . . . . . . . . . zm50

## OUR MULTI-POCKETED CAPE LETS YOU KEEP DOZENS OF MAGICAL AIDS WITHIN ARM'S REACH.

Colorful and comfortable, our 100% fugron cape is amply cut for complete neck and shoulder freedom (order your usual size). All 24 pockets are fully lined and allow the wary wizard to carry protection against evil without feeling weighed down. Special creature pocket with vents and waste disposal slot is a Frobozz Magic Exclusive.

**Cape available in most Guild colors.**

Enchanter's Cape: Small, Medium, Large. . . . zm23
Monogram available . . . . . . . . . . . . . . . . . . . . zm3

## TO CONDUCT BETTER MAGIC, YOU NEED BETTER WANDS.

Our uncharged wands are made from the finest materials zorkmids can buy. And they're guaranteed free of all contamination and ready for all your spells.

We have traditional oak, maple, and dogwood, as well as sleek, strong new metal wands. All wands available with or without handle, finished or unfinished. Wands are transported in special magic-resistant packaging to eliminate troublesome spell intrusion. For special woods and other materials, write or call. We've been making wands to order for over 200 years.

Oak, unfinished (specify with or without handle). . zm44
Maple, unfinished
(specify with or without handle). . . . . . . . . . . . . zm49
Dogwood, unfinished
(specify with or without handle). . . . . . . . . . . . . zm52
Finished wands add . . . . . . . . . . . . . . . . . . . . . . zm8

## IF MAGIC FAILS TO PROTECT YOU, TURN TO THE BLADES THAT WILL.

Ensure your safety any time, any place, by carrying a super sharp blade from the Frobozz Magic Sword division. Sure, magic is a more sophisticated means of protection. But wouldn't you rather look a little behind the times than risk getting munched by an unfriendly Dornbeast? All blades are hand-honed for balance and symmetry.

**Choose from three blade sizes: Regular, Heavy, and Very Heavy.**

Regular . . . . . . . . . . . . . . . . . . . . . . . . . . . . . zm11
Heavy . . . . . . . . . . . . . . . . . . . . . . . . . . . . . . zm21
Very Heavy . . . . . . . . . . . . . . . . . . . . . . . . . . zm29

## HAND-BLOWN FOR GREATER LUMINOUS ENERGY CONDUCTION BY FAMED GLASSMASTER YIGGAM.

This is not the mass-produced glass you used in thaumaturgical school. We commissioned Yiggam of the Peltoid Valley, glassmaster of the Antharia Guild, to create laboratory glass so exceptional, it actually improves your magic up to 25%. Yiggam shapes beakers for optimal energy conduction; tubes, too. You'll see the difference immediately. And we've sold over 450,000 pieces without one return!

Beaker .................................... zm7
Tube.......................................... zm4
Swizzle Stick .............................. zm2

---

Ordering from the Frobozz Magic Magic Equipment Catalog is fast and fun. And delivery time is minimal. Our shipping department uses the most advanced temporal travel techniques so that you get *what* you want when you order it.

---

## WE BROUGHT BACK GOOD, OLD-FASHIONED TRANSPORT BROOMS, JUST LIKE GREAT-GRANDMOTHER USED TO FLY.

*BACK BY POPULAR DEMAND!*

Our motto, "It's better to be safe than grounded," has never seemed more apropos. This dependable, economical form of transportation has been updated to include crystal ball compartment, pulsar detector, and storm shield. Fully collapsible for easy carrying. And we've cleverly disguised our transport brooms as ordinary domestic models to ward off thievery. Fully cushioned wood handle is non-skid. Nostalgia has never been more practical!

**Available in three lengths: 4 np, 9 np, and 12 np.**

4 np ................................ zm19
9 np ................................ zm23
12 np .............................. zm32

## ONLY OUR MAGIC MONITORS ARE MINED EXCLUSIVELY FROM THE CAVES OF VISION.

*SPECIAL SALE!*

Don't be fooled by shortcuts and half-measures. Today, the traditional crystal ball is one of the wizard's most important projective devices. After years of trying cheaper glass, discriminating soothsayers are coming back to crystal. We never left. Our crystals are mined from the legendary Caves of Vision, whose clarity and depth is world renowned. All our glass is flaw-free, ground to exacting tolerance, and lovingly polished.

**Available in all sizes from "egg" to "jumbo."**
**Colors available: Clear, Red, Blue, and Black.**

Egg . . . . . . . . . . . . zm34
Orange . . . . . . . . . . . . zm39
Grapefruit . . . . . . . . . . . . zm45
Jumbo . . . . . . . . . . . . zm50

## EVERY WIZARD CAP IS SPECIALLY REINFORCED TO COUNTERACT ATMOSPHERIC INTERFERENCE.

A cap so good-looking, you'd never guess it's functional too. First, our laboratory wizards developed a special impenetrable material we call Rayresistor. Then, our designers integrated this thin, flexible fabric into a cap that makes a fashion statement about you every time you wear it. Has been coated to be water-resistant.

Wizard Cap . . . . . . . . . . . . zm11
Also available with brim . . . . . . . . . . . . zm13

## MAKE YOUR MARK WITH OUR NEW DIAMOND-TIPPED SCRIBERS.

*A FROBOZZ MAGIC MAGIC EQUIPMENT EXCLUSIVE!*

Engineered for even flow and guaranteed for one life. Only our burins can withstand Frigid River Valley temperatures. And they make even the most ordinary parchment look like Flathead royal stationery. Diamond tip means toughness and versatility you can count on.

**Available in a wide range of colors.**

Burin . . . . . . . . . . . . zm19
Diamond Tips (2) . . . . . . . . . . . . zm31

## A FLYING CARPET SO RELIABLE, THE PSYCHIC STORMS OF GOMAR COULDN'T DEFLECT IT FROM ITS COURSE.

*LABORATORY-TESTED.*

You can look high and low, but you'll never find a flying carpet better than ours. Supercharged for quick pick-up and sustained pep. Foot-loomed for strength and durability. Easy to maneuver with special Contortayarn that lets you squeeze through cracks and breeze through even the densest traffic jams. Can hold up to 63,000 rps. Stone washable.

**Specify colors and design.**

Carpet . . . . . . . . . . . . zm450
Supercharger . . . . . . . . . . . . zm75

## UNIQUE ION-REVERSING TIPS MAKE THESE OUR MOST ENERGY-EFFICIENT, INVIGORATING BOOTS.

You wouldn't expect boots this attractive to be practical—but they are! As your body sloughs off energy (and you know it will), our unique ion-reversing tips capture and recycle it. And the process is so subtle, you'll feel nothing but great. You'll wonder how you ever got along without them. Exceptionally comfortable with flexible all-rubber soles and soft, rounded lugs. Fits like a glove. These are our best-selling boots ever. Please measure feet carefully, as all boots are made to order and cannot be returned. Boots . . . . . . . . . . . . . . . . . . . . . . . . . . . . zm85

## OUR TROPICAL LIZARDS ARE SENT IN OUR WORLD-RENOWNED, TEMPERATURE-CONTROLLED NEWTPAKS TO ENSURE FRESHNESS.

What can we say about the wonders of lizards that hasn't been said already? You know how essential these little creatures are for complementing spells. But did you know that the fresher the lizard, the stronger its contribution to your magic? Why not try our first-quality lizards? If you're not delighted (and we wouldn't make this offer if we weren't sure you will be) with their performance, simply return unused portion for a full refund. Keep in a warm, damp place.

6 Pak . . . . . . . . . . . . . . . . . . . . . . . . . . . . . . . . . zm11
12 Pak . . . . . . . . . . . . . . . . . . . . . . . . . . . . . . . . zm17
43 Pak . . . . . . . . . . . . . . . . . . . . . . . . . . . . . . . . zm39

# Deadline

Preface to the Story

A wealthy industrialist, Mr. Marshall Robner, locked himself in the upstairs library of his New England colonial estate one night and committed suicide by taking a lethal overdose of anti-depressants. Or did he?

You are the Chief of Detectives. You've been asked by Robner's attorney to make a thorough investigation of the case, simply to "quash the suspicions which are inevitable" when a moneyed man dies a sudden and unnatural death. The Medical Examiner found nothing unusual, and interviews with family members and family associates are consistent with the idea that Robner committed suicide. Everything fits neatly — maybe too neatly. You smell foul play, and you have 12 hours to crack the case. If you arrest someone, you'd better have the three traditional ingredients to an ironclad case for the prosecution: the accused must have had a motive, a method, and ample opportunity to commit the crime. There are many possible endings to this case, and the one you reach is determined by your actions and by the deductions you draw from the evidence you gather. But one ending fits the facts better than any other, and you will know it when you reach it.

About the Author

Marc Blank. A graduate of MIT and the Albert Einstein College of Medicine, Marc has been involved in writing interactive fiction since its formative period in the late 1970s. Co-author of the original mainframe version of ZORK in 1977, he was instrumental in laying the groundwork for the appearance of interactive fiction on personal computers in the early 1980s. He is co-author of ZORK I, ZORK II, ZORK III, and ENCHANTER, and is sole author of DEADLINE, the first interactive mystery. His continuing work in interactive technologies in large part made Infocom's name synonymous with interactive fiction. His mother still wishes he would practice medicine.

## Deadline Special Commands

*ACCUSE (someone) OF (something) - This makes an accusation against someone.

*ANALYZE (something) - Duffy, your assistant, will take "something" to the police lab for routine analysis, including fingerprints

*ANALYZE (something) FOR (something specific) - If you're looking for a specific substance on or in "something," the lab will run a special analysis.

*ARREST (someone) - If you've found enough evidence, this sentence will end the case and describe the outcome of the prosecution.

*ASK (someone) ABOUT (someone or something) - This is an impersonal form of the sentence CHARACTER, TELL ME ABOUT (someone or something).

*EXAMINE (something) - This allows you to look at something with an eye toward detail. You will probably use this a lot.

*FINGERPRINT (something) - This is the same as ANALYZE (something) FOR FINGERPRINTS.

*SEARCH (someone) FOR (something specific) - This is a search for something in particular, whether unusual or not.

*SEARCH NEAR (something) - This allows you to look closely at the area immediate to something, possibly providing more information than simply examining it.

*SHOW (something) TO (someone) - You may get an interesting reaction.

*SHOW ME (something) - A request to another person to show you or lead you to something.

*TIME - This tells you the current time of day in the story. You can abbreviate TIME to T.

*WAIT FOR (someone or some amount of time) - You may wait for some specified amount of time; if something interesting happens in the meantime, however, your wait will terminate then. You may also wait for a character to arrive; if something interesting happens in the meantime, or if the character doesn't show up after a long time, DEADLINE will ask you if you want to keep waiting

*WAIT UNTIL (time) - This causes time to pass until the desired time arrives. If anything interesting happens during this time, you will have a chance to stop waiting

*WHAT'S WRONG? - This is a request to another person to discuss what's on his or her mind

*WHERE IS (someone or something) - This is a request to another person to help you find someone or something.

# Official Memo

Lakeville, CT Police Department

July 8, 1982

RE: Evidence on File

The transcripted interviews which follow were obtained July 8, 1982. Interviewees were persons found in and about the Robner household at the time police arrived. Also attached are representations of physical evidence including fingerprints, a lab report and a photograph of the scene of the incident, which have been processed as matters of record. Taken together, the findings indicate that the deceased was suffering from acute stress due to business difficulties, possibly exacerbated by marital discord. Of particular interest is young Robner's hostile reaction to questioning; however, the undersigned would not characterize his remarks as being suspicious in nature. More probably they reflect the respondent's ambivalent feelings toward the deceased. In conclusion, it is the opinion of this investigator that all known facts show this to be an open-and-shut case of suicide by poisoning.

GK Anderson

G. K. Anderson

INTERVIEW WITH MRS. ROBNER

DETECTIVE ANDERSON: How did you come to find Mr. Robner?

MRS. ROBNER: When I woke up this morning, I noticed that Marshall was not in his bed. I wasn't alarmed, really, as it was not unusual for him to work late at night in the library and fall asleep there. I went down the hall to the library and knocked on the door. He didn't answer, so I knocked even harder. When that didn't work, I started calling his name loudly. So loudly, actually, that I woke up Mrs. Dunbar and George. We all were gathered there, knocking and yelling, and finally Mrs. Rourke, our housekeeper, was alarmed enough to come upstairs. She suggested calling the police, which we did. They arrived about twenty minutes later, and started breaking down the door with axes. When we entered the room, we found Marshall lying on the floor, face down.

ANDERSON: Did he usually keep his door locked when he worked?

ROBNER: Almost always. He was pretty secretive about his work, and he liked to be alone when he worked.

ANDERSON: Do you know of any reason why your husband might have wanted to take his own life?

ROBNER: He's been very depressed lately, you know. His business, Robner Corporation, is not doing well, and there is talk of selling out to a larger firm. Marshall founded the company, what, about twenty-six years ago, and he has been desperately trying to find some way of saving it.

ANDERSON: The pills we found by his body,do you know what they are?

ROBNER Yes. They were Ebullion tablets. It's an anti-depressant his doctor prescribed for him just last week.

ANDERSON: Had he been acting less depressed since then?

ROBNER: I really don't know. I haven't noticed much change.

ANDERSON: Did your husband ever talk of suicide?

ROBNER: He did, actually, though I never took it seriously. He would talk about how everything would be easier if he were dead, but when he would start again talking about how he was going to have to keep the business going. I'm...I'm... stunned, really.

ANDERSON: Mrs. Robner , do you know of anyone who might have wanted to kill your husband?

ROBNER: Why, no. Of course not. He wasn't a very friendly man; he was very quiet. But he was a great philanthropist, you know, and everyone that knew him respected him. I can't imagine anyone wanting to hurt Marshall. Do you really suspect he didn't commit suicide?

ANDERSON: I don't suspect anything. I just want to understand what's happened.

INTERVIEW WITH MS. DUNBAR

DETECTIVE ANDERSON: You were Mr. Robner's personal secretary, is that right?

MS. DUNBAR: Yes, sir.

ANDERSON: I understand that you were the last person to see Mr. Robner alive. Could you tell me about that?

DUNBAR: Why, yes. I brought him some tea at about 11 PM that night.On nights when he expected to work late, he would always expect tea at that hour. I brought him the tea and he asked me to leave. That's all.

ANDERSON: Did Mr. Robner seem at all upset?

DUNBAR: He did appear quite nervous, but he had been upset for some time, as you know.

ANDERSON: Do you know what he was working on that evening?

DUNBAR: No. I wasn't with him, except for that one time.

ANDERSON: Do you recall whether the pills, the Ebullion pills, were on the desk when you came in?

DUNBAR: No, I don't remember that.

ANDERSON: Ms. Dunbar, were you with Mrs. Robner when the door was opened by the police?

DUNBAR: Yes.

ANDERSON: Do you remember her reaction? Anything she might have said?

DUNBAR: She didn't really react much. I don't think she said anything except "He's dead," or something of that sort. She just stood there with the rest of us until you people arrived.

ANDERSON: How were the Robners getting along? I mean, were they happily married?

DUNBAR: I don't think so, really. He was so quiet and, well, dreamy. She was always scolding him for paying too much attention to the business and to his "good works." They rarely went out lately, which seemed to upset Mrs. Robner quite a bit. She had friends of her own that she used to visit. I think she would have gone insane, otherwise.

ANDERSON: Thank you, Mrs. Dunbar. Oh, one last thing. You prepared the tea for Mr. Robner?

DUNBAR: Yes, I started the water boiling about a quarter of, and then poured the tea when I heard the whistle from the living room.

ANDERSON: You weren't in the kitchen during that time?

DUNBAR: I just told you no.

ANDERSON: Was anyone else awake in the house while you were waiting?

DUNBAR: Yes, I believe that both George and Mrs. Robner were awake. I remember George coming down, reading for a bit, then retiring.

INTERVIEW WITH MS. DUNBAR (cont.)

ANDERSON: Do you believe anyone might have a reason to kill Mr. Robner?

DUNBAR: No, I can't imagine

ANDERSON: Thank you Ms. Dunbar. Oh Ms. Dunbar, were you at home all night, last night I mean?

DUNBAR: Well, no, actually. I was out with a friend last night and we didn't get back until 10:30 or thereabouts.

ANDERSON: Thanks again, Ms. Dunbar.

INTERVIEW WITH MR. BAXTER

DETECTIVE ANDERSON: You were Mr. Robner's business partner, is that correct?

MR. BAXTER: That's right.

ANDERSON: How long have you and Mr. Robner been partners?

BAXTER: For about twenty-five years now.I was his partner almost from the start of the business.

ANDERSON: Mrs. Robner tells me that there have been problems lately with the business. Could you tell me what that's all about?

BAXTER: Yes, the business has its problems, some of them quite large. Marshall and I were working on a plan to solve those problems and get the company back on its feet again before we would be forced to take drastic action. I hope that I can hold things together now that Marshall is dead. He was the founder of the business and controlled many things by himself.

ANDERSON: Did Mr. Robner ever talk to you about personal problems, or how he felt?

BAXTER: No, we were business partners, not intimate friends. I don't think he really had any close friends. I know he had gotten himself very upset about the business, but that's the extent of it.

ANDERSON: When was the last time you say Mr. Robner?

BAXTER: Yesterday afternoon, at our office in town.

ANDERSON: And where were you after work?

BAXTER: Last night was my concert night at the Hartford Symphony. I go there quite regularly. After the concert, at about 10 o'clock, I went home. I received a call from Ms. Dunbar this morning telling me of the tragedy, and I arrived here just a few minutes ago.

ANDERSON: Were you at the concert alone?

BAXTER: Quite alone.

ANDERSON: Do you know of anyone who might have wanted to harm Mr. Robner?

INTERVIEW WITH MR. BAXTER (cont.)

BAXTER: No. Except for George, of course. During some of their shouting matches I've heard George threaten Marshall, but I don't really think he ever would have followed through.

ANDERSON: Shouting matches?

BAXTER: George and Marshall were always at odds. You see, George has been living like a spoiled child all of his life. He's twenty-five now and has never held a job. Just spends money, or gambles it away. Being the Robner's only child, he gets away with murder. Marshall would lecture him and threaten to cut him off without a cent, and then the yelling would start. Eventually Marshall would give in.

ANDERSON: When was the last time you heard this?

BAXTER: Actually, I heard it again just last week. Strange, now that I think of it, they went at it just last week. I hear that Marshall told George that he had decided to disinherit him. He even mentioned it to me at the office the next day. He seemed pretty serious. I suppose that the financial troubles at the company may have been responsible for his attitude.

ANDERSON: Are you at the house often? You say you have heard some of the 'shouting matches.'

BAXTER: Well, I'm really not here often. Only on occasion. I have heard it once or twice and have been told of other times.

ANDERSON: Thank you, Mr. Baxter.

INTERVIEW WITH MRS. ROURKE

DETECTIVE ANDERSON: Mrs. Rourke, how long have you been working as housekeeper for the Robners?

MRS. ROURKE: Ever since the house was built, six years ago.

ANDERSON: Tell me all you remember from the night of the murder.

ROURKE: I remember that by about 10:30 or so...

ANDERSON: You mean 10:30 PM.

ROURKE: Yes. By 10:30 when I went to my room to do some reading, everyone was upstairs excepting Ms. Dunbar, who had just returned home. She went upstairs at about 11, bring Mr. Robner his tea. He almost always takes his tea at 11. I remember saying goodnight to her on her way up, and that's the last I heard until this morning, with all the shouting and banging going on upstairs. No, that isn't right. George was downstairs also for a while, only about 10 minutes or so.

ANDERSON: Could someone have gone upstairs during the night?

ROURKE: I don't rightly think so, at least not before 3 or 4. You see, I like to do some reading late at night, and I was reading this really exciting mystery story, and, lord, I was up until nearly 4 o'clock before I finished. and who do you think the murderer was?

INTERVIEW WITH MRS. ROURKE (cont.)

ANDERSON: Really, Mrs. Rourke, let's stick to the matter at hand. Do you keep your door closed at night when you are reading?

ROURKE: Yes, sir.

ANDERSON: So then it's possible that someone might have entered the house and gone upstairs without your knowledge.

ROURKE: No, sir. I don't believe so. Why don't you try the stairs yourself? For a new house, these stairs are the noisiest I've ever heard. My door's right beside them, too. When the Robners owned a little cat, I can remember hearing every footstep creaking up the stairs. Don't know why they don't ever fix it up. I guess it don't bother them any.

ANDERSON: But it is possible that someone might have entered after you went off to sleep.

ROURKE: Well, I suppose it might be, but not before.

ANDERSON: How long has Ms. Dunbar been living here?

ROURKE: Ever since the place was built. She does an awful lot of work for Mr. Robner, you know. I don't think he could have gotten along without her, although that's not my business to say. He was always so nervous, fretting about everything, and forgetting to do this and that. It seemed that she was always covering his tracks, if you get my meaning.

ANDERSON: Do you have any reason to suspect anyone of wanting to harm Mr. Robner?

ROURKE: Well, of course I've heard all of the screaming and fussing with George and Mr. Robner. That's been going on for years, now, so I don't make much of it anymore. No, I can't imagine anyone wanting to hurt poor Mr. Robner. He was such a sweet man.

ANDERSON: Thank you, Mrs. Rourke.

INTERVIEW WITH GEORGE ROBNER

DETECTIVE ANDERSON: Mr. Robner, I have been told by Mr. Baxter that you and your father had some serious arguments lately. Could you tell me what they were about?

GEORGE ROBNER: I don't think that's your business.

ANDERSON: I'm told they had to do with you habit of wasting or gambling away your father's money.

ROBNER: So?

ANDERSON: I've even been told that he threatened to disinherit you.

ROBNER: Yeah. He said he was going to. I'll bet he didn't, though. He never has.

ANDERSON: Mr. Robner, let me be frank. I'm told that you threatened violence against your father as recently as a week ago, and now he's dead.

ROBNER: Look, I don't get what you're driving at. You find the poor guy dead in his room. The room was locked. His bottle of medicine is nearly empty. What sort of detective are you, anyway?

ANDERSON: I'm doing the asking, if you don't mind.

ROBNER: Then ask someone else.

NOTE: G.R. left abruptly at this point.

# Lab Report

Lakeville, CT Police Department

Case: Robner, Marshall

File #: H657/SJ43.1

Officer of Record: Detective G.K. Anderson

Mat'l(s) analyzed: Porcelain teacup

Analyzed for: Fingerprints, foreign substances

Date: 7/8/82

Laboratory findings:

The teacup was analyzed. The cup contained tea only. No trace of Ebullion or other substances was found. Fingerprints on the cup belonged to the deceased and Ms. Dunbar.

# Official Memo

Lakeville, CT Police Department

File # H657/SJ43.1

G.K. Anderson, Detective 1st Class

July 8, 1982

RE: Robner Case

Although it appears that at least one member of the Robner household had a reason for wishing Mr. Robner dead, the findings of the Medical Examiner and evidence gained from interviews with the family and family associates are only consistent with the conclusion that Mr. Robner died of a self-administered overdose of Ebullion.

GK Anderson

G.K. Anderson

Chief of Detectives
Edindale Police Department
Edindale, CT 06103

July 9, 1982

Dear Chief:

I must once again ask for your assistance on a case involving one of my clients.

As you are no doubt aware, Mr. Marshall Robner, the industrialist and philanthropist, was found dead yesterday morning in his home. As far as I can determine, he was found dead on the floor of his library, the victim of an overdose of Ebullion, a medicine which he had been taking lately for severe bouts of depression. He had been alone during the night, and the door to his library had been bolted from the inside. Police had to break the door down with axes, I'm told, to get inside.

While I am completely convinced that there was no foul play involved in Mr. Robner's death, it is disturbing that Mr. Robner had called me only three days earlier for the purpose of informing me that his will was to be altered. In fact, I was expecting to hear from him this week so that he could deliver the papers to me. Given the size of the Robner estate, I feel that a more complete investigation should be undertaken, if for no other reason than to quash the suspicions which are inevitable in these circumstances.

I phoned Mrs. Robner this morning and informed her of my intention of having you take on the case. She was reluctant to be of assistance, but I convinced her to allow you to come around at eight o'clock tomorrow morning and spend the day.

I will be at the house at noon tomorrow for the reading of the current will, which Mr. Robner wrote a few years ago. I hope to see you then.

Sincerely yours,

Warren Coates

Warren Coates

Coates, Shavely & Coates • Attorneys at Law • Suite 1327 • Excelsior Tower • Hartford, CT 06101

# CORPUS DELICTI

**Union Memorial Hospital, Lakeville, CT**

Summary of findings from Coroner's Examination

| Name | File No. | | Date |
|---|---|---|---|
| Robner, Marshall | H657/SJ43.1 | | 7/8/82 |

| Sex | Race | Color of Eyes | Color of Hair | Ht. | Wt. | Distinguishing Marks |
|---|---|---|---|---|---|---|
| Male | Caucasian | Brown | Gray | 5'11 | 192 lbs. | None |

Apparent Cause of Death
Drug overdose (Ebullion)

Front

Back

There were no injuries or marks of a suspicious nature, except a small bruise on the left temple (consistent with falling to the floor from a chair).

Analysis of the blood of the deceased revealed a blood level of 27mg% for Ebullion. The therapeutic range of this drug is normally 4 to 6mg%. A fatal dose, while not specified by the manufacturer, has been found to be in the 10-20mg% range. A routine analysis for other common drugs was unproductive.

Findings were unremarkable except for massive liver damage consistent with overdose of Ebullion, and 10mg of Ebullion recovered from the stomach. Death occurred at 1 AM, plus or minus one hour.

The blood level of Ebullion and the massive liver damage consistent with Ebullion toxicity lead to the inevitable conclusion that the deceased died of an overdose of that drug.

Xaviera Hockmuller MD.

Medical Examiner

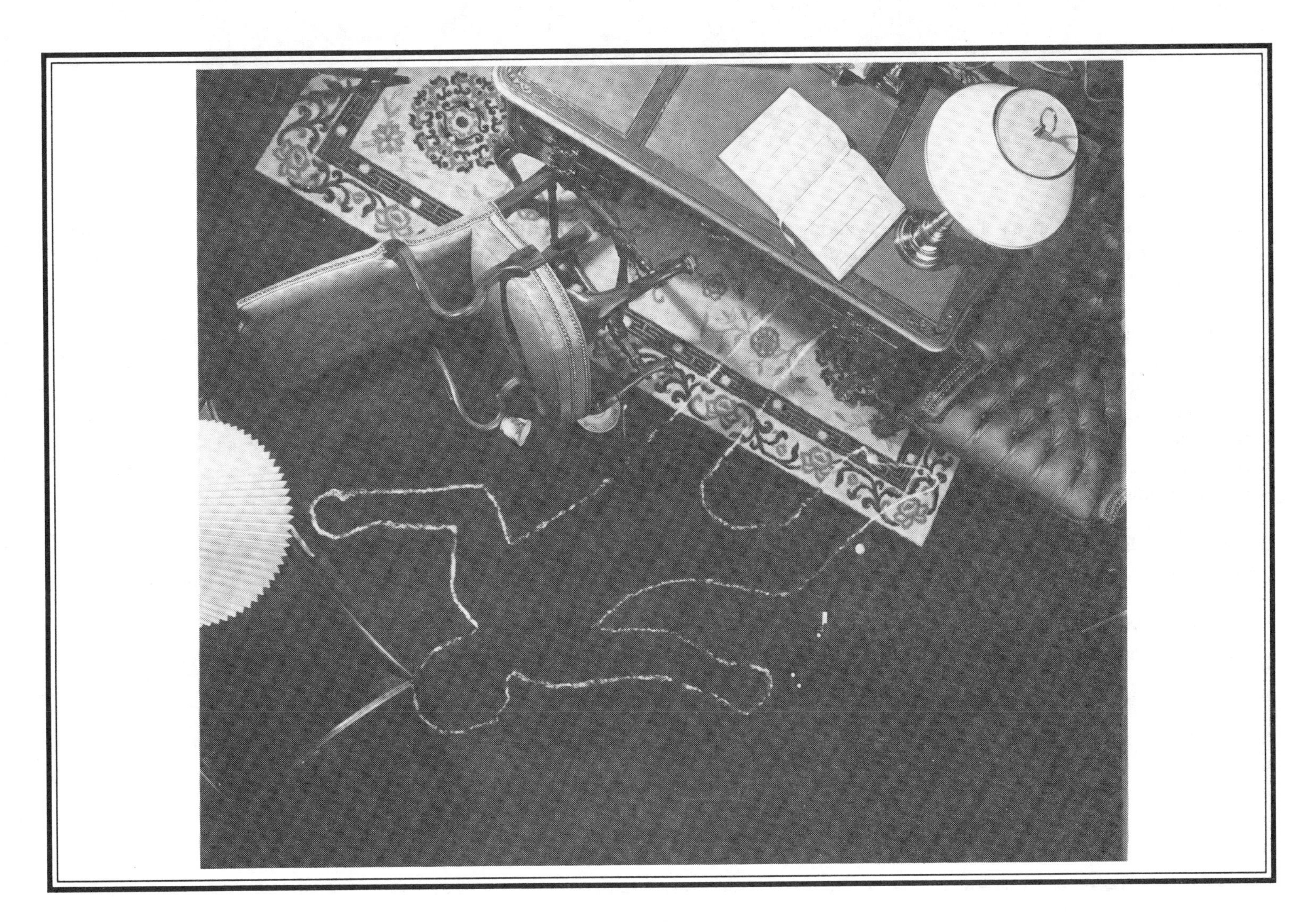

# Witness

Preface to the Story

In The WITNESS, you are a police detective working near Los Angeles. The year is 1938, and on this stormy February night a wealthy but frightened man has asked you for protection. In spite of your best efforts, a death will occur, and you will have twelve hours to solve the mystery and try to arrest the killer. If you think you have enough evidence against one or more suspects to convince a jury of their guilt, you can arrest them and conclude the case. Your ever-helpful assistant, Sergeant Duffy, will assist you in taking the accused into custody. (He will also offer help before the arrest if you ask him for it.) You can expect to receive a letter from your superiors about the outcome of the grand-jury investigation — and, if the District Attorney gets an indictment, of the trial itself. If the jury does not convict, your higher-ups will probably tell you where you may have erred, so that you can profit from your mistakes. Because the State cannot win the case unless it can prove guilt beyond a reasonable doubt, you are expected to establish the three traditional ingredients to an irondclad case for the prosecution: the accused must have had a motive, a method, and ample opportunity to commit the crime. There are many possible endings to this case, and the one you reach is determined by your actions and by the deductions you draw from the evidence you gather. But one ending fits the facts better than any other, and you will know it when you reach it.

About the Author

Stu Galley was a student of physics and journalism when he discovered computers, which at the time were mostly just big number-crunchers. At first he thought computers were too much fun to be taken seriously, until he decided that physics was too little fun to be taken seriously. At MIT he discovered computer games and Lisp-like languages and met the other founders of Infocom. He began writing interactive fiction in 1982 and has authored The Witness and Seastalker, both for Infocom.

**Witness Special Commands**

*ACCUSE (someone) OF (something) - This makes an accusation against someone.

*ANALYZE (something) - Duffy, your assistant, will take "something" to the police lab for routine analysis, including fingerprints.

*ANALYZE (something) FOR (something specific) - If you're looking for a specific substance on or in "something," the lab will run a special analysis.

*ARREST (someone) - If you've found enough evidence, this sentence will end the case and describe the outcome of the prosecution.

*ASK (someone) ABOUT (someone or something) - This is an impersonal form of the sentence CHARACTER, TELL ME ABOUT (someone or something).

*CONTINUE - This is the same as RESTORE.

*EXAMINE (something) - You will probably use this a lot.

*EXAMINE (something) CAREFULLY - You will probably use this occasionally, when you think that spending more time will give you more results.

*FINGERPRINT (something) - This is the same as ANALYZE (something) FOR FINGERPRINTS.

*REVISION - This is the same as VERSION.

*SEARCH (someone or something) - This is a search for unusual items.

*SEARCH (someone) FOR (something specific) - This is a search for something in particular, whether unusual or not.

*SHOW (something) TO (someone) - You may get an interesting reaction.

*SUSPEND - This is the same as SAVE.

*WAIT FOR (someone or some amount of time) - You may wait for some specified amount of time; if something interesting happens in the meantime, however, your wait will terminate then. You may also wait for a character to arrive; if something interesting happens in the

*When Mr. and Mrs. Bob Lundstrom of Great Prairie, Minnesota, had their first telephone installed in their home last April, they celebrated by making calls to neighbors all over the county. This wonderful invention was a gift from God. Until late one November night when the 'phone rang and the Lundstroms received their first. . .*

# DEATH THREAT!

## LAW ENFORCEMENT GETS TOUGH WITH DEVIANTS WHO PLAGUE THE "PHONE LINES.

"Five a.m., I was lying in my bed trying to decide what to do next," recalls Bob Lundstrom. "My wife kept asking, 'who was that calling, Bob?' And I kept answering over and over, 'It was nobody we know; a wrong number for someone named Minkinin.'

"Eunice knew there was something more to it than that. She knew because I couldn't fall back to sleep after the call. I kept hearing the voice, a southerner's voice, over and over in my head. 'Lundstrom, watch your behind you, don't stay out after dark and don't let me catch you in St. Croix Bluffs ever again - or your a dead man!'

"I didn't know what to do. It was five o'clock in the morning, and it didn't seem like it would do much good to call the sheriff that night. I had no idea where the 'phone call came from or who was behind it.

"All I knew was that I was scared and a bit mad. I haven't felt that powerless since the German bombing raids in the World War. It could be a prank. But then, you can bet I'd think twice before I showed my face in St. Croix Bluffs after dark again. I was a gun-shy man. I had to talk to someone. So after three or four days of agony, I called the FBI.

## TOUGH TALK AT THE TOP.

Authorities at the telephone company and at the Federal Bureau of Investigation have been plagued by a rash of what authorities are calling "the telephone intimidators" -people who use the nation's 'phone systems to scare or abuse innocent citizens with life-threatening or obscene 'phone calls.

Up until this year, the menace was not widespread enough to warrant a full-scale investigation. But now J. Edgar Hoover's G-men are attacking the problem with a crack squad of electrical experts who, working with engineers at the Bell System and Western Electric, hope to bring the plague under control in the near future.

"We're going to bring 'phone abusers to justice," says Hoover. "Already legislation is pending in the House and Senate that will make telephone threats and abuse a Federal offense."

While most of the reports of 'phone abuse are prank calls, a great number are actual threats on people's lives. Take, for instance, the case of Mafia boss Louis Gambognini, who died last year in a hail of bullets outside his Providence, Rhode Island, fortress. His last words were made to one of his aides as he stepped out of the front door of his mansion: "The punks are threatening me over the telephone now. Can you believe that? They say they're going to gun me down." But cases like Bob Lundstrom's are more the norm. Readers will be happy to note that Lundstrom's case turned out to be nothing more than a random 'phone call made from a crossroads diner just outside of Great Prairie.

"It was probably just a drunken truck driver on his way back to Mississippi," said FBI Midwestern Director of Operations Harold Pinkolt.

"The point is that if victims respond quickly enough, we may have time to respond quickly enough, we may have time to trace the call back to its origin and nail the perpetrator," Pinkolt says. The FBI is putting together an elaborate tracer system that Pinkolt says "will nail the offenders in a matter of minutes," Sources close to the story say that the new tracer system - code-named "Operation Infocept" -is still a long way from being indefectible.

An FBI agent in Minneapolis, who demanded anonymity, detailed this exclusive story for the *Nat'l Detective Gazette.*

"We spend a lot of time sitting around playing gin rummy, you know. Shoot, my first assignment in Minneapolis was a stakeout that lasted nine days, and the guy wasn't nowhere near the building we were watching. But this 'Operation Infocept' is really something. See, we're trying out this new tracer system, and we got our first call from a panicky housewife out in Stillwater, who said she got a call from someone who was going to kidnap her the next time she went down to the drugstore for a soda. Well, instead of asking questions, we hooked right up into the system and traced the call back to a house out in Dellwood. So we - me and five other fully armed agents - sped out there in hopes of catching the punk red-handed. We should have known something was fishy when we showed up at 38 Lakeland Drive, and it was a beautiful two-story Colonial. But we didn't have time to think about all that. We busted in the front door, and all we found was this woman with her baby fixing dinner and listening to the radio. I guess the system traced the 'phone call to the wrong place, because that lady sure didn't seem like she'd be making threatening 'phone calls. We never did get our man. But you know, we're still working out the kinks.

"The kicker is, we come to find out later that the lady who had been threatened didn't even drink soda. And that she lived out in the sticks, about thirty miles from the nearest drugstore. She only went into town about once a week!"

Director Pinkolt had little comment on this particular case. He said only, "As with any new crime-solving accessory, it takes some time to perfect the system. We don't let minor mishaps deter us from our goals."

Meanwhile, back in Washington, Director Hoover has set a five-year deadline for the total implementation of 'Operation Infocept.' Criminologists here at the *Gazette* and at police departments all over the country eagerly await new developments in the field of electric surveillance and interception. Hover promises not to let us down.

National Detective Gazette

# INVESTIGATIVE MACHINES *of the Future!*

by Raymond Klotz, D.Cr.

*The days of Flash Gordon, Private Detective, may not be so far off as we think, theorizes the controversial doctor of criminology. In this excerpt from his futuristic commentary,* 1985, *the good doctor hypothesizes an outlandish answer box that makes us wonder: will machines one day rule the world?*

The day will come - perhaps not in our lifetimes, but surely in the early part of the next millennium - when machines will be *the* most important tool of the detective's craft.

This prediction, which I have named the *Pathos Parabola Hypothesis* (PPH), has been a hotly contested issue ever since I first presented it at the American Criminologists Conference in 1934. Veteran detectives have been laggard in accepting the inevitability of this cataclysm. But careful deduction and rational extrapolation bear out the validity of the PPH.

*Editor's note: Dr. Klotz uses many big words. But he refused tp let us edit his column on the grounds that it would, as he says, "enervate the verisimilitude of my contentions" -whatever that means.*

One day machines with brains - not flaccid gray cerebellums, but brains of humming wires, trembling electrodes and glowing cathodes - will be doing the exhaustive legwork of ten, even fifty hawkshaws. The crime lab will be replete with unctuous robots and eager automatons. But real heroes will not be these machines; on the contrary, they will be the honest men and women who build and operate the machines. They, together with their whirring, beeping mnemonic devices, will be the ones who abrogate crime in the next millennium.

*Editor's note:What the doctor is trying to say is that pretty soon you're going to be solving crimes with machines. And if you don't like that, try a baseball bat.*

To the doubters and denigrators who remain impervious to my predictions, I offer a whole host of *already existing* technological achievements that provide proof of the ceaseless procession of the techno-sophisticative march into the future! The radio: where would any metropolitan police force be without it? Yet, only twenty years ago, when the first commercial broadcast came over KDKA Pittsburgh, there were thousands who believe it would never last. The telephone: ten years ago, had you any conception of the powers of surveillance and intercept that the telephone provided? Today, would any law enforcement agency be able to survive without the everyday 'phone tap? And you may have gazed in astonishment at the newest wonder machine, the so-called television. Who would have thought that one day a visual panoply of optic enchantment would oscillate unseen over the airwaves? And who, ten years from today, will deny the incredible powers of surveillance and eavesdropping that the television provides?

*Editor's note:Dr. Klotz's so-called "television" does indeed exist. Whether or not it can be of assistance in the apprehension of criminals remains to be seen. Klotz"s opinions are not necessarily the opinions of this publication.*

At this point, the Pathos Parabola Hypothesis is irrefutably valid. But, as with any brilliant concept, there comes a juncture where what is known must be relegated to the back of our minds and what is recondite must be explored. So, for a moment, suspend what is known, unharness your inhibitions, unfetter your foregone conclusions and imagine the next great invention...THE ELECTRO MAGIC BRAIN (EMB).

*Editor's note:As this issue goes to press, Dr. Klotz has exiled himself to Walla Walla, Washington, where he continues his EMB research. Much of the scientific community has discounted this portion of the Pathos Parabola Hypothesis. But in the Nat'l Detective Gazette tradition, we print even the most segments of the doctor's postulates.*

National Detective Gazette

As a scientist and a moralist, I am not at liberty to divulge the details of my 10-year employment in the service of our FBI. Suffice to say that the Bureau maintains some type of dossier on every man women and child in these United States of America.

One day, all the information that is contained in these files will be electro-machanically sealed inside the circuits of gigantic Electro Magic Brains. At the issue of a single cryptic voice command, such as "OKLIT VOS FROB VEN-VEN DOOBELDEE." the brain will regurgitate reams of information stored within its vast memory. Smaller versions of the brain will be linked to the main-brain through an extensive wire system called a "meshwork." And these micro-brains will be able to communicate with the main-brain in a special brain language known to only a select few law-enforcement officials throughout the nation. Information will be permanently stored on tiny ticker-tape machines using a binary code of dots and dashes similar to Morse Code. Other codes will be organized into logical packages of information and commands that determine what the machine does. These packages will be bundled together into crime-solving "programs."

Obviously, the minute details of the Electro Magic Brain's operation and utility remain in question. We are still in the conceptual stages of development. Yet, the powers that be in our vast national security service have deemed the EMB the vanguard of our future efforts in crime control for the next millennium. I, for one, have no misgivings about the plausibility of the Electro Magic Brain. Its day is coming. Those who fail to utilize the potentials of tomorrow will be living in the past. I implore detectives everywhere to heed this message.

*Editor's note:The Nat'l detective Gazette has begun to see the wisdom of some of Klotz's predictions. We have just acquired two mechanical adding machines for our accounting department.*

# TIPS FOR GREENHORNS

*Domestic squabbles can cause two things—ulcers and death. Heck, think about it . . . you got a kitchen full of knives, forks and various blunt objects. And you got a couple of red-hot lovers who aren't asking for a third opinion . . . you know what I mean?*

National Detective Gazette

**by Capt. Jock Barnes**

Give me five minutes of your time, and I'll tell you a story that will make you think twice about bustin' up a love nest. I'm going to relate the details of just one case to you. I think it gives you a pretty good idea of what the heck danger is. If you haven't learned anything after reading this, you ought to consider going back to selling ladies' shoes at Montgomery Wards.

I used to work with a guy named Paul Kelly. I liked that guy a lot; I walked a beat with him for six years. The Barriom, Watts. We even did a few weeks; detail down at Muscle Beach. We were friends. We used to drink together. He and his wife Paula used to come over on Saturdays, and we'd drive up the coast to Atascadero where we used to swim. That was a long time ago. Paul's dead now. I watched him die because of our stupidity. I watched a man sink a rusty screwdriver into his gut while I lay half-conscious on the kitchen floor of a grimy little apartment in east L.A.. It was a pointless murder. One that shouldn't have happened.

It started as just another simple domestic case. It was August - hot as a grasshopper's rear-end in a brush fire. A woman called the precinct about six o'clock one Saturday evening all in a conniption. She said her husband was trying to kill her because she was messing around with the milkman or some such nonsense. To tell you the truth, I don't remember. Paul and I were in the area, so we checked it out. It was half hour to shift change, and we didn't feel like making an evening of it, if you catch my drift. We didn't case the joint before we went up. That was our first mistake. Before we knew shucks for Shinola, we were backed up against the kitchen wall with a sawed-off shotgun dancing lullabies before our eyes. I noticed a picture of the Pope hanging on the wall behind the guy with the gun. Very comforting.

Paul was on my left, next to the kitchen table. I stood beside him facing the guy. Behind me was an open door and a hallway leading off into the living room. We had to think fast. I started talking to the guy, telling him he didn't need the gun. We were only there to answer the complaints of his wife, who at this time I didn't see. I though for a minute that the guy might have already bumped her off, so I started to get a little scared, thinking he didn't really have anything more to lose by knocking off a couple of cops. I looked at Paul and knew right away what he was thinking. He was ready to go for the guy's gun if I could just distract his attention for a split second. I asked him if he and his wife needed to see a marriage counselor or something. He laughed at me and then started getting mad. I guess he didn't like the idea of me and Paul busting up his little party. While I was trying to calm the dude down, Paul gave a little head fake and went for the gun. Paul was quick as sin. He used to play semi-pro ball with the Escondido Onions. I saw him get hold of the barrel just as it exploded. I went down like a ton of bricks with an incredible blow to the head. I thought I was hit when I looked up I saw the lovely housewife standing over me with a rolling pin. She had opened up a pretty big gash in my noggin, and I was dazed bad. I could see Paul across the room struggling with the dude. The gun had sprayed wide, but Paul still managed to take a couple pellets in the arm. The guy had him down on the floor and was reaching for a screwdriver when I started to yell. That was the last thing I remember. The old lady cuffed me again with the equalizer and the next thing I knew, I was in the hospital. Paul died from the stab wounds. And that was that.

O.K., so what's the moral to the story? You figure it out. There we were, two cock-sure cops with a combined experience of a whopping twelve years. It was Saturday night, and we didn't feel much like hanging around the zoo. We were impatient, clumsy and stupid. We paid a high price for it, too. You don't have to.

Always case a joint before you start busting down doors. See who's who and what's what. Play it cool; don't be a jerk. People don't like jerks - especially jerks in uniform. These domestic squabbles *never* have to end up like this. Just have a little consideration for the parties involved. They don't want spectators at their fistfights. They get mad easy. they're already mad. that guy, Johnny Cordoba, he didn't *mean* to kill Paul. And his wife there, sweet Suzy with the rolling pin, she was probably getting ready to take it out on Johnny when we happened to walk in. So I ended up getting the wood. It just goes to prove that in the heat of passion, people like that will strike out at anything and anybody. So don't get in their way. You're a referee, not a participant. But that doesn't do Paul any good now. Johnny Cordoba's up at San Quentin for the next 60 years making license plates, and Paul is gone. It didn't have to happen that way. Don't let it happen to you!

*Captain Barnes is a retired LAPD veteran who walked the Angel City beat for over 40 years. He now lives with his wife June and his dog Fang in retirement in Redondo Beach.*

National Detective Gazette

# L.A. gumshoes rate the watering holes.

There are jock bars, jazz bars, junker bars and jive bars. But where do off-duty L.A. detectives go when they need a moment's reflection and a stiff drink? Our west Coast *Gazette* staffer surveyed over a hundred law-enforcement types and asked them to pick the five best bars in the area.

1. The Condor's Nest, 2424 Caristas Springs Blvd., L.A. Far and away the favorite, this dark and secluded haven has everything but a snooker table.

2. The Shasta Lounge, Beacon Court, Hollywood. For the best selection of single malts and imported ales, you can't do any better than this.

3. Fish Camp, MacArthur Wharf, Long Beach. Longshoremen and the law mix in this unpretentious warehouse bar. Cheap.

4. The Bel Pre, 4162 Gardena Rd., Torrance. L.A.'s darkest and most secret rendezvous.

5. The Brass Lantern, corner Berez and LaVezza, San Fernandito. Where all good cops go when they need to get out of town. Try the Moo Goo Gai Pan!

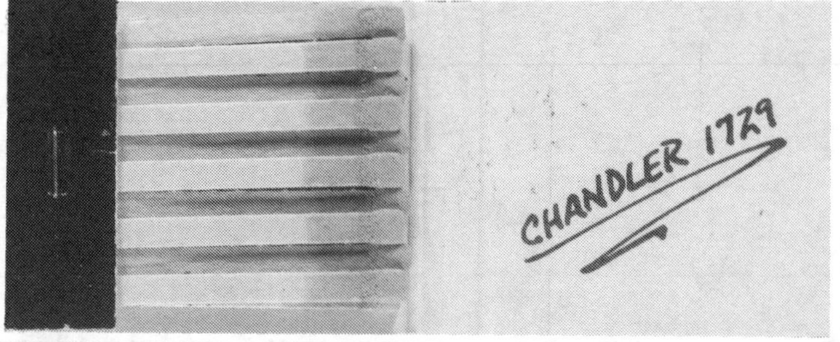

# BALL GOES ON WITHOUT GUEST OF HONOR LINDER

**Amidst diamond-studded society hoopla, the Los Angeles Charity Ball went on last night without Goodwill Ambassador of the Year Award recipient and keynote speaker Freeman Linder. He was unable to attend due to the tragic shooting death of his wife on Sunday (see related story Page 2, Column 8).**

Linder's absence didn't seem to dampen the spirits of the other 800 party-goers at the fifty dollar-a-plate, black-tie affair. Motion picture mogul Gaunt Rockwood served as emcee for the event, which was attended by local civic and social leaders.

Standing in for Linder was his long-time business associate and traveling companion Yukio Matsuyama.

Matsuyama, a Japanese businessman who immigrated to the U.S. in 1920, delivered a captivating speech about Linder's life-long love affair with the peoples of the Orient.

Linder, the 10th recipient of the award, has been active in Asian business and charities since 1900 when he was stationed in China as a marine. His business, Pacific Trade Associates, is an international import-export company devoted to the exchange of goods between the U.S.A. and Asia. After founding the company in 1922, Linder spent 13 of the next 15 years in Tokyo, Hong Kong, and Peking only returning home sporadically to see his family. Through this Asiatic association Linder has developed a strong tie with the languages and culture of the region. On his infrequent returns to Los Angeles, Linder has given almost all of his energies to Asian Charities. In fact, in a speech he delivered several years ago

**(Continued on Page 2, Column 8)**

The Register

SANTA ANA, CALIFORNIA, TUESDAY, FEBRUARY 1, 1938

54 Leading Daily Drauss Ca., pop. 148,000 (est); Santa Ana pop. 98,000 (et) Established 1908 "Blade" Merger 1918.

# LINDER ABSENT FROM AWARDS FETE

**(Continued From Page 1)**

Linder said that he felt closer to his adopted Asian families than he did to his own. During his extended absences his wife had served as director of the Asian-American School and Cultural Center, the largest institution of its kind in the United States. Linder started the school in 1925.

Mr. Matsuyama spiced his delivery with accounts of Linder's exploits during his early days in the Orient. As a marine, Linder took part in the Boxer Rebellion in Shanghai in 1900. In 1904, he returned to the States and tried to fit into the coat-and-tie working world. However, his adventurous lifestyle lured him back to Hong Kong, where in 1907 he was rumored to have contracted as a "for hire" mercenary. In 1910, he returned home to marry and start a family only to be drawn back to Tokyo soon after. There he served as a civilian engineer in the Japanese Navy between 1912 and 1922. During that period he became a personal friend of Hirohito, who is now Emperor of Japan. An illness in Linder's family forced him to return home in 1922, at which time he founded Pacific Trade Associates. Within the year he was back in the Orient.

Partygoers were transfixed by Matsuyama's discourse on the problems that face the Asian people in this country and what Linder has done to help alleviate those problems. Mr. Linder is a self-taught multi-lingual whose never-ending dedication to the causes of social justice has made him one of Los Angeles' most admired and successful businessmen.

Near the end of his address, Matsuyama invoked the prayers of those attending the ball for the soul of Linder's wife, Virginia. She was found dead in their Cabeza Plana home Sunday, the victim of a gunshot wound. Police are investigating the incident, but thus far no arrests have been made.

Proceeds from the ball will go towards the establishment of a new youth center in downtown Los Angeles.

Monica Dearest—

I can live with this sadness no longer. For twenty-nine years, your father has lived his own life without me. Now I am taking the only way out.

Monica, you musn't blame yourself in any way for what I am about to do. Nor should you blame Ralph. The affair with him was only a futile attempt to prove I was a woman, not just a piece in Freeman's collection.

Tell your illustrious father how deeply I regret soiling one of his precious revolvers.

Mother

CLASS OF SERVICE

This is a full-rate Telegram or Cablegram unless its deferred character is indicated by a suitable symbol above or preceding the address.

# WESTERN UNION

1201

SYMBOLS

DL = Day Letter

NL = Night Letter

LC = Deferred Cable

NLT = Cable Night Letter

Ship Radiogram

R. B. WHITE
PRESIDENT

NEWCOMB CARLTON
CHAIRMAN OF THE BOARD

J. C. WILLEVER
FIRST VICE-PRESIDENT

The filing time shown in the date line on telegrams and day letters is STANDARD TIME at point of origin. Time of receipt is STANDARD TIME at point of destination

Received at 001 FR YS LOSANGELES CA 02-18 849A PST=

PMS CHIEF DETECTIVE=

POLICE HEADQUARTERS=

CABEZAPLANA CA=

BELIEVE STILES ENDANGERS MY LIFE STOP URGENTLY REQUEST=

YOUR ASSISTANCE STOP PLEASE COME TO 4986 LYMAN DRIVE=

AT EIGHT THIS EVENING STOP=

FREEMAN LINDER=

CONF 4986==

RECEIVED CBPL Q

915A PST 1938

# Suspect

Preface to the Story

Halloween night. You are a guest at a very exclusive party: the annual Costume Ball at Ashcroft Farm. You are mingling with society's blue bloods and power brokers, sampling caviar and champagne, and enjoying the fine orchestra and the outlandish costumes. Quite a treat for a newspaper reporter like you — until someone plays a nasty trick on you. You're framed for a murder you didn't commit. You'll have a hard time convincing the police of your innocence. You'll have to figure out who did commit the heinous crime, and why. You'll need irrefutable proof. The murderer is no doubt watching your every move. But you have only a few hours to escape the trap that's been laid for you.

The murderer is in your midst, laughing behind your back.

About the Author

Dave Lebling was born in Washington, D. C. and grew up in suburban Maryland. He attended the Massachusetts Institute of Technology, and worked at MIT's Laboratory for Computer Science, where he developed an interest in computer entertainments. He was a co-author of the original mainframe Zork. He has co-authored Zork I, Zork II, Zork III, and Enchanter, and written Starcross and Suspect on his own

### Suspect Special Commands

*ACCUSE (someone) OF (something) - This makes an accusation against someone.

*AGAIN - SUSPECT will usually respond as if you had repeated your previous sentence. Among the cases where AGAIN will not work is if you were just talking to another character. You can abbreviate AGAIN to G.

*ASK (someone) ABOUT (someone or something) - This is an impersonal form of the sentence CHARACTER, TELL ME ABOUT (someone or something).

*CONTINUE - This lets you continue on to wherever it was that you were going. You can abbreviate CONTINUE to C.

*DIAGNOSE - This will give you a brief description of your physical condition.

*EXAMINE (something) - You will probably use this a lot.

*EXAMINE (something) CAREFULLY - You will probably use this occasionally, when you think that spending more time will give you more results.

*GO TO (a location) - This command starts you on your way to a specific room; it will take you there one move at a time and will tell you what rooms you're passing through and what events are happening there. Once you're on your way, you can continue on to your destination by typing CONTINUE or C at subsequent prompts.

*SEARCH (someone or something) - This is a search for unusual items.

*SEARCH (someone) FOR (something specific) - This is a search for something in particular, whether unusual or not.

*SHOW (something) TO (someone) - You may get an interesting reaction.

*TIME - This tells you the time in the story.

*WAIT FOR (someone or some amount of time) - You may wait for some specified amount of time; if something interesting happens in the meantime, however, your wait will terminate then. You may also wait for a character to arrive; if something interesting happens in the meantime, or if the character doesn't show up after a long time, SUSPECT will ask you if you want to keep waiting.

*WAIT UNTIL (time) - This causes time to pass until the desired time arrives. If anything interesting happens during this time, you will have a chance to stop waiting.

*You are cordially invited to*
*the gala Halloween Ball*

*Mr. and Mrs. Michael Wellman*
*request the pleasure of your company*
*at the Halloween Ball*
*on the thirty-first of October*
*at half after eight o'clock.*

*Ashcroft Farm*

*R.S.V.P.*
*318 Oak Manor Lane*
*Crofton*

*Appropriate Halloween Dress*

Dearest...
It has been too long since
we last talked. Please do try to come
to the party. There are so many things
I have to tell you. Until then,
Veronica

**The Washington Representative**

*from the desk of*

*Earl Davis Jackson, Editor*

Since you've already been invited to this big society bash, why not go ahead and make a story out of it for our Sunday Living section?

From the looks of this article, there may be an angle that hasn't been covered. Perhaps... The Old Hunt Club types fleeing the onslaught of suburbia. Could play it either straight or humorous depending on what you get.

Enjoy,
Earl Davis J.

# MARYLAND

R A M B L E R

## There Goes the Neighborhood.

*As suburbia spreads out, Maryland's Blue Bloods move on.*

ON THE FIRST SATURDAY OF EACH month, privileged equestrians from Montgomery and neighboring counties gather at the Eaton Hills Hunt Club dressed in scarlet coats, white cravats and black velvet bowlers. At precisely 8:00 a.m., a copper horn sounds a muted but distinct tune signalling the hunters to mount their horses. On cue, 40 eager hounds sing out their own baleful music. Pulling eagerly at their chains, they, too, are ready for another Eaton Hills fox hunt to begin.

"Very soon all this will be gone," says former Maryland Senator Daniel Horn, standing in a dewy field on a crisp October morning presiding over this Saturday's hunt. "Only 20 years ago, the Allison Club (a former thoroughbred farm, now defunct) bordered us to the east, and Sharp's Hill lay to the south." Horn points off to the south, and one can see the roofs of homes interspersed through groves of oak and pine; there are not a lot of homes, not inexpensive homes, but homes nonetheless.

"There was plenty of acreage and plenty of solitude then," he says. "But now look at it. There are too many people, too many houses. In a few years, we'll be staging hunts in people's backyards. Or not at all!"

**BY SUE ANNE FRANK**

*A sign of the times: Estate breakups change the face of Maryland's past.*

PHOTO BY RALPH KING

The Allison Club, Sharp's Hill and a handful of other private sanctuaries for the rich—once sprawling farms of hundreds, even thousands of acres—have been replaced by "planned communities," as club members derisively call them. Estates formerly belonging to some of the nation's wealthiest families have been transformed into two- and three-acre plots for the upper middle class who have graduated from the fashionable suburbs of Bethesda and McLean to the more pastoral climes of Montgomery County.

New projects in this part of Montgomery County by no means cater to the impecunious. Prices for new homes start at around $250,000 and go to over a million dollars. Still, the old and sometimes intractable super-rich find it hard to coexist with their new neighbors. Begrudgingly, many of them move on; and as they go, they leave more and more of the old estates open to new development.

**The new money.**

Real estate developers such as Montgomery County's William Cochrane, a firebrand entrepreneur who buys land from the wealthiest and sells to the wealthy, have adjusted comfortably to the new order that the past 10 years have wrought. Sitting behind the wheel of his vintage 1938 Dodge "Woodie" overseeing the survey and division of his latest acquisition, the Old Sewell House, he

# RAMBLER

seems oblivious to the slow-boiling controversy that surrounds him.

"It's very simple," says Cochrane. "My clients are looking for a few acres and solitude. They don't need half a county; one or two acres will do. So they come to me. I have half a dozen properties now under development. The people who sold me this property sold it because they grew weary of fighting the inevitable. They realize how close DC has become. They know their property is worth a fortune. They know more and more people are coming, like it or not. And they know that if they can't get used to having neighbors, they're going to have to move. When they make that decision, they come to me. I pay top dollar, and I charge top dollar."

Cochrane has no romantic illusions about the Maryland Hunt Country. He plays a numbers game. And he often wins. But lately, Cochrane is beginning to feel the heat of a handful of old residents who refuse to be bullied and bought out.

A group of old-money landowners has formed a coalition to save what's left of the Hunt Country life; they are making no concessions to Cochrane and others like him. Their weapons? Money and influence.

**The old money.**

1980 Census records indicate that Montgomery County's median household income is just over $70,000. Compared to the national average of $20,000, this makes Montgomery County one of the five wealthiest areas in the nation. Interestingly, the greatest concentration of this vast wealth lies in the hands of perhaps 20 or 30 families like the Ashcroft-Wellmans.

The power and influence of this elite group of landowners extends far beyond the county line. Records on file at the Montgomery County Courthouse list at least nine influential national legislators

*(continued on page 117)*

THE KEYHOLE

**Veronica's Bash**

"What is Halloween without the pumpkins?" asked Veronica Ashcroft-Wellman as she surveyed the unloading of a thousand of the 30-pound orbs onto the front lawn of her verdant Montgomery County estate. The jack-o-lanterns will be part of an elaborate prop for one of the country's most fabulous Halloween balls to be held next week at Ashcroft Farm, Veronica's ancestral home.

*Veronica: Party Queen*

The annual ball, a 110-year-old Ashcroft tradition, draws hundreds of dignitaries from the worlds of art, business and politics. Last year's guests included Senator Lance Duncan, actor Robert McCarron, Katarina Ostrovsky of Metropolitan Ballet fame and British ambassador Sir Edward Black. And if Veronica has her way, this year's party will be even more spectacular. It promises to be second to none for sheer opulence.

Guests will dine on the rare delicacies of French Nouvelle Cuisine prepared by Master Chef Louis LeClerc of Washington's Ma Maison Restaurant. They'll be entertained by the famous Foggy Bottom Band under the direction of Vince Goodman, who, by the way, was a long-time friend of Veronica's late father Cyrus Ashcroft III. And they'll come bedecked in costumes that make Hollywood's most garish productions seem pale by comparison. To all this, add the setting of Ashcroft.

The farm, a sprawling sanctuary of pine and oak forest and pastureland, commands over 120 acres of Montgomery County's most idyllic vistas. Dominating all this is Ashcroft Manor house, built by Veronica's great-great grandfather in 1872. The farm is one of the county's last remaining colonial estates of this grandeur, and Veronica has maintained it in the finest tradition.

"I have a vested interest in this countryside," says Veronica. "Once a year I like to share the magic of this place with my friends. And what better time for magic than Halloween?"

Magic may be just what Veronica needs, because once the idle chatter has waned, talk is sure to turn to the sweeping changes that are afoot in Montgomery County.

The director of Ashcroft Trust and a close personal associate of the Ashcroft family, Colonel Robert Marston, talked to our Keyhole reporter about those changes.

*Marston: Here To Stay*

"Of course land is an issue in Montgomery County these days. Veronica makes no secret of her desire to stop the influx of new residents to the county. She sees it as being the only way of preserving her way of life.

"The many friends and relatives who will be attending this year's party are fully supportive of her position. They, too, want Ashcroft to endure as the tradition it has grown to be in the past century. That will certainly be a topic of conversation at the party."

The Halloween Ball at Ashcroft—regardless of the 'political weather'—promises to be a grand old time. For how many more years that will remain true, one can only guess.

# KING'S POINT
R E A L T Y

*Specializing in finer homes since 1868.*

WILLIAM COCHRANE
*Owner*

One Saddle Oak Square
Rappanoc, Maryland 23393
555-7721

Veronica—
Please call me ASAP.
Don't do something you'll regret.
Bill

# COSTUMES UNLIMITED
"FROM ABRAHAM TO ZORRO,
WE'VE GOT YOUR COSTUME."

312 WISCONSIN AVE. ROCKVILLE, MD
TEL. 555-9009

NAME Cash
ADDRESS
CITY

| QUAN. | DESCRIPTION | DATE | PRICE PER DAY |
|---|---|---|---|
| 1 | Cowboy Costume with lariat and gunbelt | 10/29 | $65.00 |

**004216**

TOTAL $65.00

*Deposit required on all rentals.*
*Ten dollar charge for late returns.*

Five dollar cleaning fee for costumes returned soiled.

# INTRODUCTION

*Murder can rear its head in the most inappropriate places—weddings, cocktail parties, the theatre—even in your own home. Killers, it seems, have utter disdain for social convention and proper manners.*

*Ironically, the most unfortunate aspect of a grisly murder is not the loss of a loved one, but the burden of social responsibility and proper behavior the survivors must bear. There are questions of etiquette, accusations to make and deny, puzzlement about proper dress and ironclad alibis to fuss over. The potential for social blunder is immense. Unless, of course, you are prepared to meet the challenges with finesse and sensitivity.*

*Read* MURDER AND MODERN MANNERS *and you'll soon be in complete command of even the most vile affairs. You will waltz through the proceedings while others crawl and weep. You will learn to integrate the dark underbelly of the criminal pathos into your subconscious. You will learn to deny even the most well-founded accusations. You will slander your own best friends without compunction. And, should circumstances deem it necessary, you will learn to graciously accept life imprisonment without remorse. And without parole.*

***J.D.W. October '84***

# CHAPTER ONE

## Accepting an invitation to a murder.

### The thoughtful guest.

An invitation should be answered promptly in writing using the third person. For instance, you, Mr. Charles Edwards, would reply: "Mr. Charles Edwards thanks Mr. and Mrs. Armstrong for their kind invitation to the ghastly murder to be held at Armstrong Manor on Saturday, the 30th of June, and has great pleasure in accepting.".

This formal reply is often accompanied by a more personal handwritten note that can be included in the envelope with your acceptance. (See *Why a written reply?*)

### The importance of punctuality.

Since you may be the unfortunate guest of honor, your presence might make the difference between a fabulously successful homicide and a merely great party. Under *no* circumstances, however, should you reply using the pre-printed card that accompanies the invitation. It only convinces the host of your pedestrian upbringing and propels him or other guests towards more heinous behavior on the night of the party.

### Why a written reply?

In recent years, the telephone has nearly eliminated the courtesy of a written reply. This is wrong.

A written reply, especially a fond note, gives blood-hungry investigators a bit of meaningful physical evidence. For example, the victim might be found lying dead with your note in his pocket. And if you've made that note temptingly personal, as suggested in the first part of this chapter, you've assured yourself the distinction of "prime suspect." Something like this might be nice:

"Dearest, I long to see you again. There has been too much between us these past few years." With this note, you might be perceived as an old lover with a vengeance. Or the police might infer that your sweet message was enough to drive an already distraught victim over the edge, making suicide a viable possibility.

Now, had you replied with a simple telephone call, none of this would have been possible. There would be no scathing rumors, no heated court battles. No allure.

## Special considerations.

Once you've opted to attend the party, some background work must be accomplished. Make your acceptance known among your friends and neighbors. Describe in detail your past tempestuous affairs with the host (or hostess), real or imagined. Visit a gun shop and purchase several boxes of ammunition and inquire lovingly about "that little snub-nosed .38 that would be great to have around for special occasions."

Make it clear that your intentions for attending are more complex and sordid than anyone's reason for attending a party could possibly be. Put tantalizing images in people's minds, and you've assured yourself a sensational headline in the following day's newspaper: *MODEL CITIZEN TURNS KILLER!*

Imagine if you were forced to bear the embarrassment of unflattering press coverage like this: "He was a perfectly normal fellow, quite quiet and reserved. He rarely went out; I think he was a bit of a wallflower." With a bit of pre-planning, you can have your neighbors describing you like this: "He was absolutely dashing and reckless. We called him 'Hollywood.' Some of the stories he told me about his love affairs were quite racy. An exciting fellow; I guess he just had a side to him that most normal people never experience."

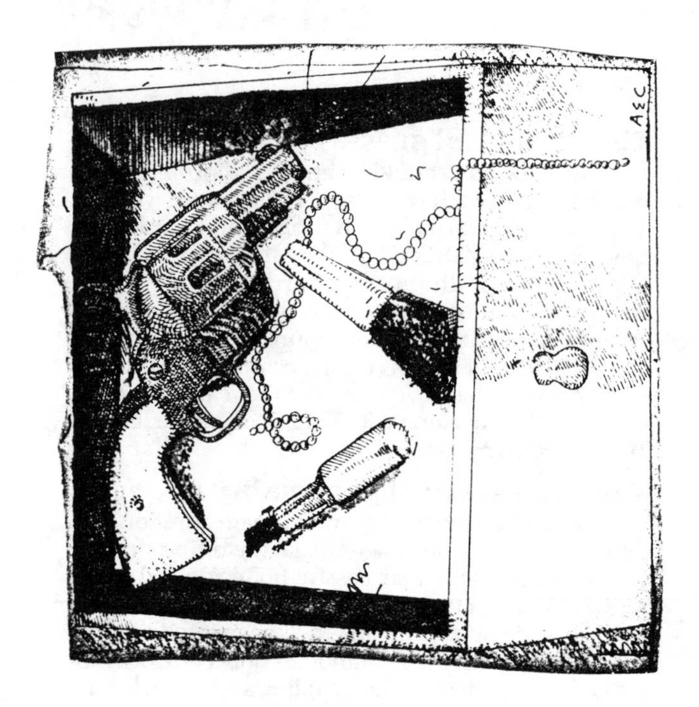

# CHAPTER TWO

## What to wear *(men)*

## Neckwear.

The most important part of a man's outfit is his tie. Besides its utility as a strangling tool, it says not only who you are, but how much abuse you're willing to take. Finely crafted silk, while appropriate at most parties, can be detrimental to a murder.

This becomes painfully obvious when a detective arrives and grasps you firmly by the tie in preparation for beating a confession out of you. Most law enforcement veterans prefer suspects to wear heavy wrinkle-proof rayon-dacron blends that won't look tattered and shopworn after a session of serious interrogation.

Should an officer clutch your expensive but frail Sulka Silkie—or even worse, a clip-on—and jerk it vigorously, it may come apart in his hands. The policeman then becomes disturbed and severe. You're inviting a kick in the shins from his canoe-sized, insulated, oil-resistant clodhoppers—a fate that can be avoided by a few minutes of foresight when choosing your tie.

## The Suit

Like tie selection, the choice of a suit is a matter of practicality. You'll be spending quite a lot of time on the floor of a cold jail cell rolled up in the fetal position. So you'll want a suit that is both warm and durable. Convenience dictates a wash-and-wear three-piece business suit. You may be wearing it for 48, maybe 72 hours in the slammer, so get something that will still look fresh when they take you to court for the arraignment. Dark colors, usually burgundy or a chocolate brown, are good for hiding cell grime and blood. No well-bred suspect can afford to wear anything less.

## Smart shoes.

High-top Naugahyde wing-tips are both functional and stylish. The steel-toed models, while sometimes hard to find, are ideal for self-defense in the lockup. They work as well as policemen's clodhoppers, yet they add an element of sophistication to even the most mundane outfit. Again, color is important. A burgundy or dark brown masks blood stains much better than a pair of suede saddle shoes.

# CHAPTER THREE

## *What to wear (women)*

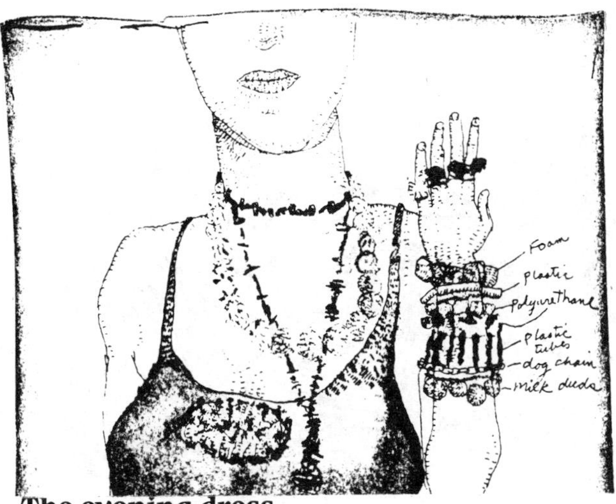


### The evening dress.

When selecting a gown, never underestimate the suspicious nature of the authorities. You may be accused, arrested and taken downtown for a suntanning session under a very powerful heat lamp. So dress accordingly.

Most women prefer something that gives them an innocent, demure look. A loose-fitting wrap or chemise is comfortable and cool, yet it belies the presence of the high-powered weapons that many women like to carry in metropolitan environs. The perfect solution for the occasion.

### Jewelry.

Nothing catches eyes and turns heads like a vault of rare gems worn by an attractive woman. However, when there's a murderer about, the last thing a woman wants is attention. One need only consider the violent ends met by such diamond-studded beauties as Czarina Alexandra and Marie Antoinette.

Here again, let form follow function. Let the lessons learned by others serve as your precedents. When you seek to make a statement with your ornaments, say it with paste—the gaudier the better. Fake opals the size of walnuts, brooches that resemble peanut brittle during a nuclear meltdown, any Cub Scout arts-and-crafts project—gimcrack of this ilk, too long overlooked by the trendsetters of High Society, is *de rigeur* as regards the lady for whom being the hit of the party is secondary to getting home in one piece. Not only will your gewgaws discourage the killer intent on robbery, they'll prove more effective than mace in repulsing any jealous ex-lover, scorned admirer or sex slayer with even an inkling of fashion sense. Remember, when you prefer not to make the Society pages at the expense of making the obituaries, junk jewelry is a girl's best friend.

### Shoes.

You can't run very swiftly in high heels. But then, you can't kick very effectively with sneakers. A sensible solution is to seek out a pair of Italian-designer jogging shoes. These combine a comfortable flat crepe sole with a toe that resembles the tip of a cross-country ski.

# CHAPTER FOUR

## Conversation, Interrogation, Incarceration.

### Opening conversational gambits.

The *first* art of a good conversationalist is the ability to put people at ease. Once you've accomplished this, you can begin to make good conversation. Your job as a pacifier and confidante is doubly complicated by the victim's knowledge of his or her impending doom. How does one allay the fears of a hapless murder victim?

You might start with a flourish of light-hearted foolery. Try hiding in the coat closet and scaring the daylights out of the victim as he opens the door to hang his coat. Or try a more conventional and earnest approach. Explain who you are: "Good evening, I'm Charles Edwards. I'm an emergency room surgeon. Have you ever been in an emergency room on Saturday night?" Now that you've got the conversation started, let it follow its natural course.

Practice is the best way to polish your conversational skills. Many beginners have difficulty at first. But rest assured, it's not really as important as you might think. After all, the victim will soon be dead. So if you fail to calm his fears, it is not going to matter anyway.

## Interrogation: Chatting with the police.

***Yes Sir!*** Authorities, like royalty, should be treated with deference. Always refer to them as Sir, Ma'am, Officer, or Your Highness. All questions should be answered with a humble "Yes, sir," or "No, ma'am." And only under the most stressful situation should you direct questions back at your interrogator—when a gun is pointed at your head, for example.

The art of a good conversationalist is the ability to "lighten up" the atmosphere at times like these. There are a few simple and time-tested rules to follow. 1. The order of questioning should start with family-related matters. 2. Once the "ice has been broken," the subject should be either sports or sex. 3. Never ask authority figures about their jobs or salaries. This is considered *déclassé* and invites additional charges of bribery and slander.

## A proven example.

Imagine for a moment that you have been arrested by the police. You are face down on a plush ballroom floor, the officer's knee rests firmly on your kidneys and his .357 Magnum is pointed at the base of your cerebellum. Light conversation might improve your situation. "So, sir, I trust that the wife and young ones are doing well?" He jabs the nose of his gun deeper into your skull.

Don't be alarmed. You've "broken the ice," so move on to the next subject.

"Say, officer, I'm certain you couldn't have missed that slug-fest of an Orioles game last night!"

The magic has begun to work. Watch as the officer takes his gun from your neck, grabs it by the barrel and cuffs you firmly across the knee cap with the finely oiled walnut grip of his beloved pistol.

There now, you've managed to get even the most ruthless authority to drop his gun from its threatening position! You've played him into your hand, and you're on your way towards a close friendship with a person who, only a few moments earlier, was a bitter enemy.

Patience, practice and perception; nothing can replace these three keys to successful conversation.

## Comfortable incarceration.

***The gang's all here!*** Let your memory drift back to the days of youth. Whether you're a man or woman, from the city or country, you must certainly have fond memories of the long summer days of your childhood. Prison is a throwback to those long lost days. You never have to work if you don't want to, you can play basketball and lift weights all day, and when you need the close companionship of a friend, there is always someone there. Someone who sympathizes with your plight. Someone who'll set you up. A good prison is just like a poorly run summer camp.

The secret of successful incarceration is connections. Upon arrival you should watch the other inmates closely. See who dominates and who submits. Then align yourself with the bullies. You'll always be assured of the best food and drink. And the best seats in the house for inter-prison boxing matches.

## Prison projects.

After two or three years in a maximum security prison, you'll become more reflective. You've got "time to kill," as they say, and you'll want to develop some of those skills that you never had time for as an overworked free adult.

The key to selecting the right pursuits is to choose those that show the greatest signs of rehabilitation, or those that will supplement your meagre weekly income as a license-plate maker.

Poetry can be a wonderfully sensitive medium for expressing your remorse and anguish. The study of law will help you improve your oratory skills, a clear benefit when you make vehement pleas to the prison parole board. Writing books can also be quite rewarding: the first eight editions of this book were all highly successful and sold particularly well among guilt-ridden liberals. But perhaps the wisest choice is painting. Prisoners are perceived as having great depth of repressed artistic genius. There are literally thousands of deep-pocketed dilettantes who are willing to pay a fortune for prison art. Especially if the work is being done by prisoners with a background of violent crime.

# A FINAL THOUGHT

## Preparedness.

In these few pages, we have touched lightly on the subjects that have, for centuries, remained nebulous and unsettled. Now that you have a working basis for confronting murder and its many-faceted elements, it's time to move ahead. It's time to seek out a party that promises to be fraught with wickedness and deceit and to plunge into it with vigor. Only then can you truly appreciate the appropriateness of this lesson. Only then will you be able to conduct yourself in a manner befitting a homicide SUSPECT.

The end.

## About the Author.

*Jane Darling Worthington lives in Maryland and South America. Ms. Worthington was educated at the Emily Post Extension University in Ghanzi, Botswana, Retenue Academe in Clambridge, Massachusetts and The Attica Reformation Institute in Attica, New York. Ms. Worthington is currently at work on her new book,* Death without Commitment.

## About the Illustrator

*Alan E. Cober, artist, illustrator and social critic, had his own ideas about SUSPECT and* Murder and Modern Manners. *And since he's one of today's most widely acclaimed graphic artists, we asked Alan to put those ideas onto paper for this SUSPECT package. He did.*

*Alan's name and works are well-known in graphic art circles worldwide. His work has appeared in TIME, LIFE, NEWSWEEK, INSIDE SPORTS and SPORTS ILLUSTRATED. He's illustrated books, record albums, advertisements and anything else that calls for extraordinary interpretation and execution. In doing all this, he has collected countless awards and kudos. We hope you enjoy what he has done here.*

# Lurking Horror

Preface to the Story

In The Lurking Horror, you are a student at G.U.E. Tech. You have braved a snowstorm to get to the Computer Center and finish work on an assignment. But the snowstorm has turned into a raging blizzard, and has trapped you in a complex of buildings late at night. You are not alone, fortunately ... or perhaps, unfortunately. Thus you begin the story, unaware that anything may be wrong beneath or within the veneer of the quiet campus.

About the Author

Dave Lebling was born in Washington, D. C. and grew up in suburban Maryland. He attended the Massachusetts Institute of Technology, and worked at MIT's Laboratory for Computer Science, where he developed an interest in computer entertainments. He was a co-author of the original mainframe Zork. He has co-authored Zork I, Zork II, Zork III, and Enchanter, and written Starcross and Suspect on his own.

## WELCOME TO G.U.E.!

You've probably been waiting to go to G.U.E. Tech for years--ever since you realized that science and math were more important to you than just about anything (except eating). And now here you are, in a community of people who feel exactly the same way. Of course, the first thing in your mind is academics, whether you can get a seminar with that Nobel Laureate Physics professor, how soon you can have 24-hour access to the Computer Center, whether you can get credit through a work-study program. Most of these questions can be answered by your freshman advisor or by the official student handbook.

There are plenty of other questions, however, that you should also be asking yourself, questions that your advisor will be hard put to answer. Questions like, where can you find the best pizza? Where can you find a date? Which dorms should you avoid? Should you subscribe to the meal plan? Where can you go if you're feeling our of control? This handbook attempts to answer some of these questions. Written by upperclass students, G.U.E. At A *Glance* (sometimes known as GAAG) might tell you things the Administration would rather you didn't know. But we believe that you'd find them out anyway, and that you'll be glad it's sooner rather than later...

In spite of what your roommate will tell you, G.U.E. Tech does not have the highest suicide rate in the country. However, it *is* a high-pressure school. While you're wondering what happened to the distraught student who used to sit next to you in Introductory Calculus, you might also be wondering how you're going to get through midterms without cracking up.

## G.U.E.

When things get tough, DON'T PANIC. Help is always available, and no one will think the lesser of you for seeking it. Visits to the Counseling Center don't appear on your permanent record, and complete confidentiality is maintained at all times.

One thing that just might drive you crazy is figuring out how to get around campus. While we've provided a map to help you identify the main dorm and class buildings, you probably won't feel at home until you've gotten lost a few times and stumbled back to familiar ground.

Large, underground tunnels connect most of the buildings. However many of these tunnels are very old, and a number have been closed for safety reasons. While you may be tempted to explore, DON'T risk it. Several deaths have been attributed to student explorations in the tunnels. Closed tunnels are off-limits; they're closed for a reason, and we encourage students to restrain their curiosity and keep out of them.

It's usually easiest for new students to live in a dormitory and subscribe to the school meal plan. But easiest isn't always best. In the case of G.U.E.'s food service, it's worst. Food ranges from bad to inedible, and the cafeterias are only open for a few hours around each mealtime. If you haven't signed up for the meal plan, or when you're planning ahead for next year, consider roughing it. Dorm-sized refrigerators are easy to come by, and the area supermarkets carry a wide variety of both recognizable and exotic items. When you're looking for a hot meal, check our list of favorite hangouts.

First-year students are usually stuck with whatever room they're assigned to. Flrod Bok is the best freshman dorm; Murani House is the worst. Best upperclass dorms are Berkowitz Hall and Lunce House. Chapelgate is well known as a party dorm. It's a good place to be if you like to party. It's a bad place to be if you plan to get any sleeping or studying done in your room.

Most dorms are co-ed, with men and women housed on separate floors. A few of the smaller upperclass dorms are for men only, and Stella Barton Hall houses fifteen senior women.

## G.U.E.

You'll also want to consider G.U.E.'s fraternities and sororities. Pledging takes place the first week on campus. Since each house appeals to a different type, you'll need to look into all of them to find one that's a good match for you. For more information, contact the Interfraternity Council.

Dorm furniture is strictly functional and, if you're lucky, less than 50 years old. Most students outgrow the dorm bookshelf within one semester. You can buy cheap but sturdy bookcases at Dave's Discount Decor, along with bean-bag chairs, lava lamps, and designer telephones (one current favorite, a glow-in-the-dark skull with gleaming red eyes, chortles instead of rings).

Although you'll be spending most of your time studying, it's important to remember that life exists outside of your textbooks and your computer screen. Take an afternoon to visit the Museum of Contemporary Art or the Loeffler Aquarium. Join the Freshman Drama Group of the Hellenic Club. Write a weekly column for the G.U.E. GNEWS. Take advantage of the Athletic Complex, whose weekly paddle-ball tournaments draw a lively crowd.

## SCHOOL TRADITIONS

SLUG STOMPING

Watch for the first slugs of the year and step on them.

FOUNDER'S DAY

One night during the last week of spring term, the huge bronze statue of George Underwood Edwards mysteriously disappears from its pedestal and shows up the next day in some totally offbeat spot. A certain rowdy fraternity is rumored to spend the entire year planning this prank.

FINAL SCREAM

At a designated time during Final Exam week, everyone screams in unison.

PIGEON DAY

The President rings a bell at 6 a.m. one spring morning and puts a statue of a giant pigeon on the lawn. No classes for the day; free food at night.

STREAMER DAY

Take all the toilet paper rolls from the bathrooms and throw them out of the dorm windows.

## SOME G.U.E. TECH JARGON:

frob. (noun) A thing. Useful when you have two "unspecified objects" on hand. "Stick that frob on the thing over there."

tool. (noun) A nerd. Someone who studies all the time, never taking time for a social life. (verb) To study. "I'm tooling tonight."

hack. (noun) A prank. "Painting the Dean's house pink was a great hack!" (verb) To commit a prank. "We hacked the Dean's house."

-p. (suffix) Adding the -p suffix to a word makes it a question. A derivative of the LISP computer language, where "p" indicates predicate (e.g., "greaterp x y," meaning "is x greater than y?"). Most commonly heard among tools majoring in Computer Science. "Foodp?" (pronounced "food-pee") means "Are you hungry?"

grease. (noun) Student politician. (verb) To pass a course without working on it. "I greased Thermodynamics."

rug rat (or rat). (noun) Freshman. Presumably derives from the use of this term as a synonym for child.

urchin. (noun) A local child or teenager who hangs around campus and often causes objects of value to mysteriously disappear.

curdle. (verb) To astonish, usually with a connotation of the surprise being unpleasant. "I was really curdled when I saw my final grades."

## DIRECTORY

don't forget snacks for Fri. party!

| | |
|---|---|
| Name Chris Leu<br>Address Chapelgate<br>Tel. No. x8990 | Name<br>Address<br>Tel. No. |
| Name chem lab T-TH 1-3<br>Address lab partner- Ardie Knowlton<br>Tel. No. X 2981 | Name<br>Address<br>Tel. No. |
| Name<br>Address<br>Tel. No. | Name Intro Calc<br>Address 27-302<br>Tel. No. |
| Name Mitch<br>Address<br>Tel. No. X5417 | Name<br>Address<br>Tel. No. |
| Name<br>Address<br>Tel. No. | Name password UHLERSOTH<br>Address<br>Tel. No (don't tell anyone!!) |

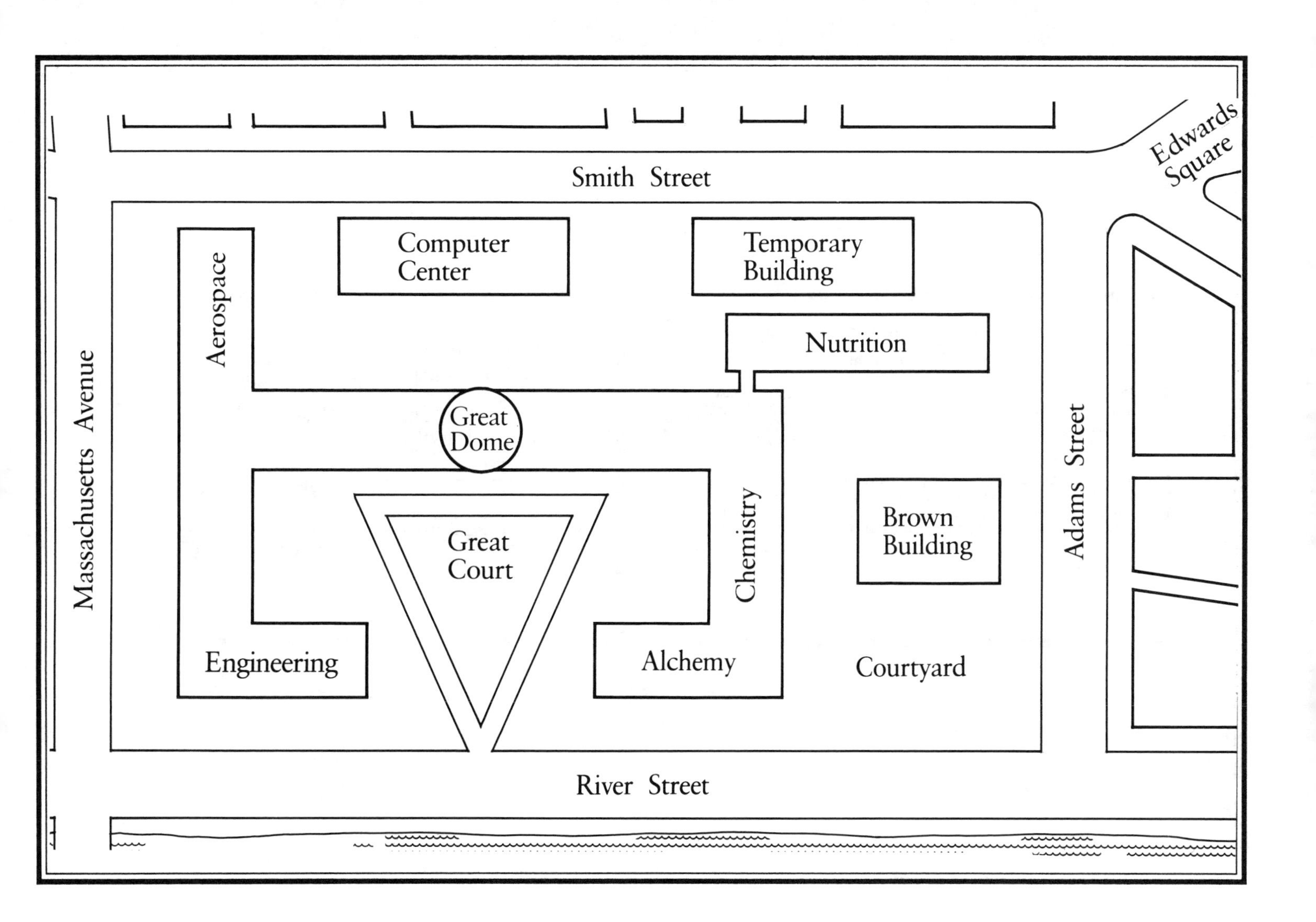
Smith Street
Edwards Square
Computer Center
Temporary Building
Aerospace
Nutrition
Massachusetts Avenue
Great Dome
Adams Street
Chemistry
Brown Building
Great Court
Engineering
Alchemy
Courtyard
River Street

**GEORGE UNDERWOOD EDWARDS INSTITUTE OF TECHNOLOGY**
**STUDENT IDENTIFICATION CARD**

This card is issued solely for your convenience. Do not allow anyone else to use it. Protect your card and code number at all times, and report any loss or theft promptly. Misuse of card, including bending, folding, spindling, or other mutilation, will result in loss of card privileges and other penalties as determined on an individual basis by the G.U.E. Tech Discipline Committee.

This is not a credit card. This card remains the property of, and if found should be returned to, George Underwood Edwards Institute of Technology. It is not transferable, must be surrendered upon demand, and may be cancelled as well as repossessed and the privileges hereunder revoked at any time without prior notice. G-IH1-ID

| SIGNATURE OF CARDHOLDER |
|---|

**GEORGE UNDERWOOD EDWARDS INSTITUTE OF TECHNOLOGY**
**STUDENT I.D. CARD**

The individual whose signature and code appear on this card shall be entitled to all stated benefits of a G.U.E. Tech student, including the use of library and cafeteria facilities. Please present card when using said facilities.

# Ballyhoo

Preface to the Story

Spurred by stinginess and your natural curiosity, you stick around after the show in the big top, hoping to catch a free after-hours performance. Perhaps you'll get a peek at an impromptu clown act, or watch the late-night feedings of the exotic animals you goggled at earlier. But life at the circus isn't glamourous after the audience has gone home: instead of flashy feats, you overhear a mysterious conversation: a little girl — the circus owner's daughter — has been kidnapped! Her father is too naive (or is he too pompously stupid?) to do more than hire an inept detective to find her. He remains blindly loyal to his overworked performers, but ... could it be an inside job? The girl might be hidden somewhere on the circus grounds ... and one of the performers might be her abductor! So you do what anyone would in these circumstances: set out to rescue the damsel in distress. The odds aren't in your favor: you — a spectator, a bystander, an outsider in a defensive close-knit community — trying to find a girl you've never met, in a place you know nothing about, among bizarre people who want nothing to do with you. Some would call you brave. Some would call you foolish. Every circus has its seedy underside. But few are as dangerous as this.

About the Author

Jeff O'Neill is a computer school dropout from Whittier, California. After graduating in 1982 from California State University, Los Angeles, he worked in journalism and for a while dabbled in computer science at a local community college. In the spring of 1984 he did the equivalent of running away with the circus by moving to Massachusetts to become a game tester for Infocom. Through diligence and hard work he finally came to fulfill the typical American boyhood dream — to get paid for writing interactive fiction. Ballyhoo is his first Infocom story.

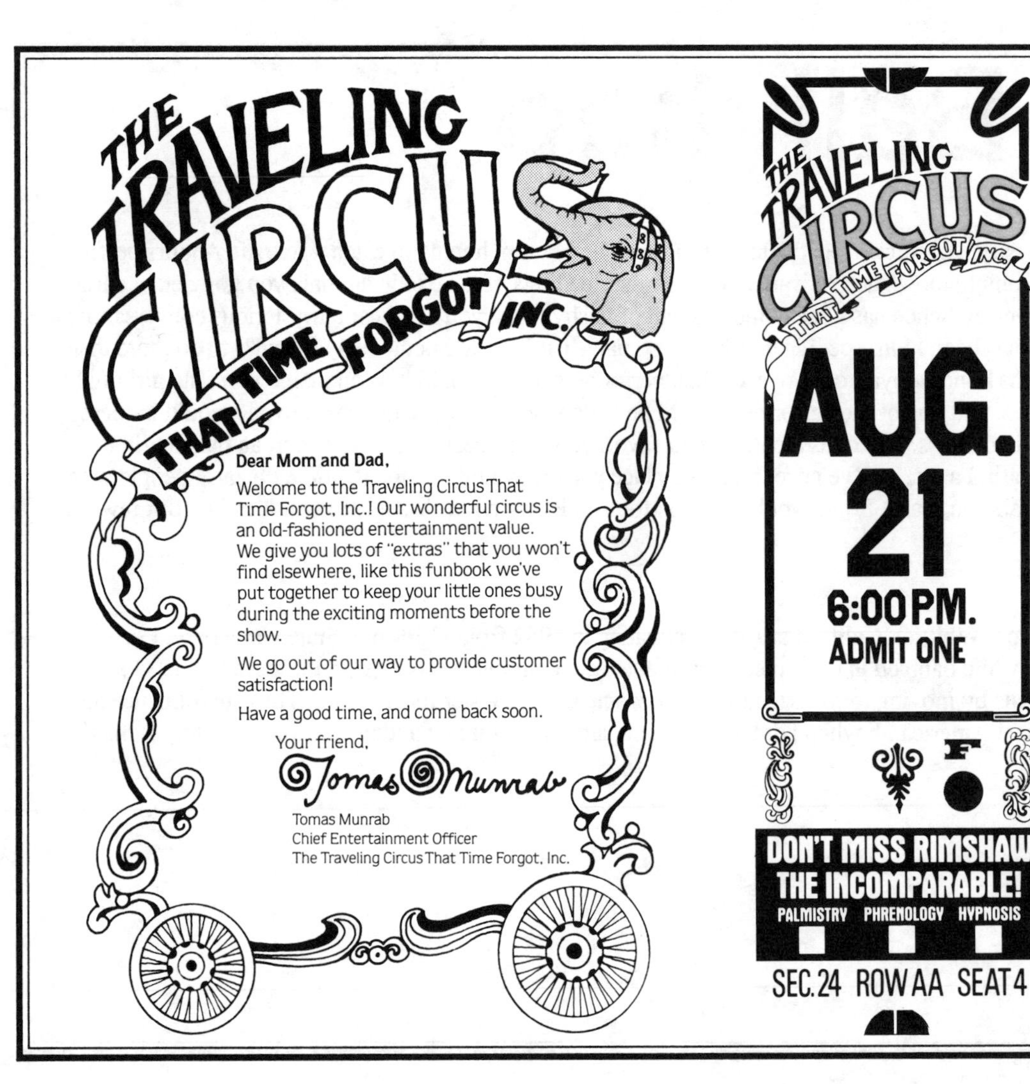


Dear Mom and Dad,

Welcome to the Traveling Circus That Time Forgot, Inc.! Our wonderful circus is an old-fashioned entertainment value. We give you lots of "extras" that you won't find elsewhere, like this funbook we've put together to keep your little ones busy during the exciting moments before the show.

We go out of our way to provide customer satisfaction!

Have a good time, and come back soon.

Your friend,

Tomas Munrab

Tomas Munrab
Chief Entertainment Officer
The Traveling Circus That Time Forgot, Inc.



THE TRAVELING CIRCUS THAT TIME FORGOT, INC. welcomes you to its two-ring extravaganza and side-show extraordinaire! You'll see feats of skill and daring, ferocious animals from the jungles of Africa and Asia, and amazing human curiosities!

This ticket also entitles you to three sessions with RIMSHAW THE INCOMPARABLE. Simply present your ticket to (1) have your palm read, (2) undergo hypnosis, and (3) allow him to read the bumps on your head.

We are committed to bringing you the best entertainment value! With this goal in mind, we're completing a series of demographic surveys. You can help us by punching out the pink (female) or blue (male) dot on the front of this ticket to indicate your gender.

The Traveling Circus That Time Forgot, Inc. is not liable for any loss of personal possessions or for any injuries or damages you might cause or personally sustain while on the circus grounds. To help prevent such injuries or damages and thus avoid the possibility of lawsuits on our behalf, we ask you to obey the following rules and regulations:

Please do not throw anything into the circus ring. Severe injury to our performers may result.

Please do not feed or attempt to pet the animals. These are unpredictable wild beasts.

Beware of pickpockets, gamblers, thugs, and thieves. We are not responsible for local criminal elements.

Please leave immediately following the performance. Do not loiter in the ring or on the circus lot.

Above all, have fun! We hope to see you again next time we're in town.

Glorious Gloria
TINA
TOMAS MUNRAB
A Man With A Vision
ANDREW JENNY
Genatossio Brothers

**How the incredibly backward vision and superlative genius of one man set into constant motion The Traveling Circus That Time Forgot, Inc.**

Put yourself in the man's oxfords for a moment. A graduate magna cum laude from one of the world's most prominent business schools. Yet at the same time, a maverick at heart, independent of mind - reluctant to follow his blue-suited classmates lockstep into the boardrooms of Corporate America. A man with vision - a vision as yet undefined, like a cloud, anticipating the release of its own charge, the lightning bolt of an idea.

So what do you do if you're an out-of-work Harvard Business School grad with a dream? You go out and buy yourself a circus, of course.

The idea, brilliant in its simplicity: to resurrect the classic traveling circus of old -blending innocence, flamboyance, and nostalgia - and send it off to crisscross the highways and byways of this promised land of ours, visiting upon the masses thirsty for good clean fun.

Sounds so simple, yet it is hard to imagine the tremendous quatum of resistance and awesome challenge that would confront this would-be modern day P.T.Barnum. Immediately you would hear the voice of the nay-sayers, their prickly criticism intended to burst your balloon, deriding such "pipe dreams" as low tech and low brow, logistically impossible, financially unfeasible. And imagine the embarrassment of getting laughed out of the HARVARD CLUB!

Now, if you ever met Tomas Munrab, you'd know one thing for certain: the word "impossible" is unknown to him. Not through any lack of education, certainly, but by willful, steadfast determination to overcome all obstacles in his life's path. A couple of years ago, it was this personal drive coupled with this vision that compelled Mr. Munrab to invest in a small circus and to completely transform it, thus embarking on the odyssey of The Traveling Circus That Time Forgot, Inc.

As President, Producer and Chief Entertainment Officer of The Traveling Circus That Time Forgot, Inc. (a wholly owned subsidiary of Munrab Enterprises, Inc.), Mr. Munrab himself has overseen whole hog the acquisition of the capital, talent, and marketing savvy necessary for transforming his circus into the growing concern you see today.

"It takes some doing to maintain an exciting family show with a genuine, turn-of-the-century feel, while at the same time funding additions, improvements, and the necessary attentions to investors," says Munrab, obviously proud of his mastery over his dual role as showman and businessman. "You could say I've had to deal with quite a few clowns over the past couple of years."

Despite such good-natured banter from the Boss, it's clear from their much-practiced performances and their dogged dedication that the circus folk hold Mr. Munrab in high esteem, even reverence.

## THE AMAZING GENATOSSIO BROTHERS

In a daring display of high wire skill and reckless abandon, the famed Genatossio Brothers thrill spectators with an array of death-defying feats. Balanced on a thin steel cable 50 feet overhead, Carlo, Giuseppe, Antonio, and Stefano Genatossio play a heart-stopping game of leapfrog, ride tandem bicycles, jump rope forward and backward, and perform a stupendous break-dance finale.

The 28-year old Genatossio quadruplets, natives of Bologna, Italy, were spotted by Tomas Munrab at a county fair in Upstate New York. After seeing their incredible performance, he asked the young men to join The Traveling Circus That Time Forgot, Inc. *"Senza dubbio,"* says Carlo, "we accept without hesitation."

# GLORIOUS GLORIA
## Queen of the Air

Not since the days of Lillian Leitzel have circus-goers been so entranced by a trapeze artiste. With her sequined tutu and halo of blonde hair, Glorious Gloria Golotov embodies the glamour and daring of the big top. Gloria dazzles audiences with an extraordinary repertoire of aerial splits, somersaults, and pirouettes, culminating in the stunning death-whirl made famous by Leitzel in the 1920's.

Glorious Gloria, Queen of the Air...captivates Crowds with her Courage and Flair ... Weaving her wondrous Aerial Spell ... Glorious Gloria ... Artiste Nonpareil!

# THE WILD KINGDOM

In 1815, Hackaliah Bailey toured New England with his elephant "Old Bet." there by creating the traveling menagerie. His show was so successful that imitations soon appeared, offering an array of exotic animals drawn from the four corners of the globe. Massive elephants from India stood side by side with savage lions from the Tanzanian plains and quick-witted apes from the jungles of the Congo.

Eventually menageries combined with circuses to produce the touring extravaganzas of the late 19th century. This has remained their place to the present day.

Crucial to the success of the menagerie is the animal trainer, who earns the respect of even the most ferocious tiger and arranges for the care and feeding of all.The Traveling Circus That Time Forgot, Inc. is proud to present world-renowned trainer Gottfried Wilhelm von Katzenjammer.

In one of the most breathtaking moments of the show, Gottfried strides bare-chested into into a cage of ferocious, snarling lions. Using only a bullwhip and chair, the fearless trainer masters the savage beasts, commanding them to perform a series of dramatic stunts.

Born in Hanover, Germany, in 1952, Gottfried is the son of famed pachyderm trainers Wilma and Werner von Katzenjammer. After honing his skills in the family act, Gottfried rose to prominence in the acclaimed Crique Martinique. He was persuaded to join The Traveling Circus That Time Forgot, Inc. in 1983, during Tomas Munrab's annual world-wide talent search.

Blond and muscular, Gottfried draws as much attention as the animals he commands. From the stunning lion act to the magnificent elephant parade, the skills of Gottfried Wilhelm von Katzenjammer and his wild animals contribute immeasurably to the excitement and pageantry of The Traveling Circus That Time Forgot, Inc.

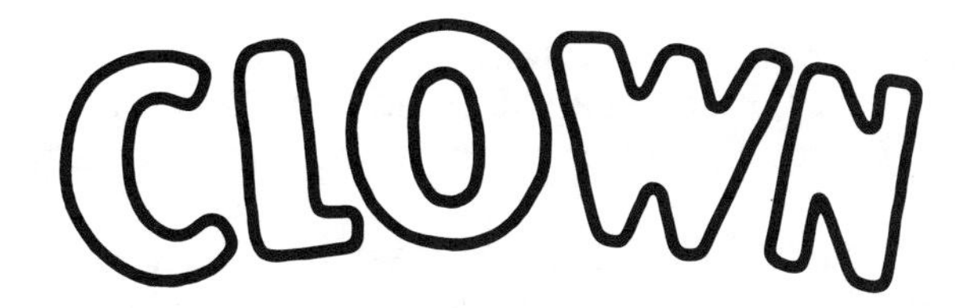


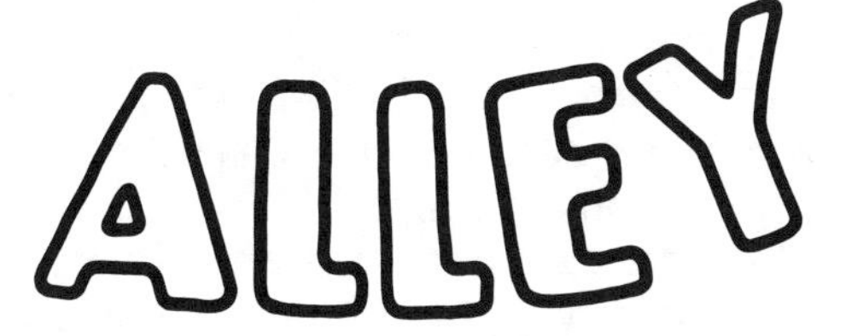


The great showman P.T.Barnum once remarked that clown are the pegs on which circuses are hung. When the atmosphere of suspense and tension in the arena approaches unbearable limits, the clowns arrive to lighten the mood of the spectators in preparation for the next death-defying stunt.

Foremost in our Clown Alley is the celebrated Comrade Constatine Thumb. Only 28 inches in height. Thumb proudly bears the title of the smallest man in the world. Born of normal-sized parents in the West Siberian Plain, Thumb was educated at the famed Surgut Acrobatics Institute. He defected in 1984, at the behest of Tomas Munrab, to join The Traveling Circus That Time Forgot, Inc. Whether cavorting with his miniature dachshund, displaying his considerable acrobatic skills, or warbling in his native Russian, our merry midget delights audiences from Dallas to Dayton.

Comic companions to Comrade Thumb are the other members of our clown troupe, from Chuckles, the buffoon tramp, to Mystic Malcom, the stumblebum magician.

All in all, the clown's profession is a noble one. The world is full of tears, and it is far more difficult to send us into gales of laughter than it is to make us cry.

# Glittering Extravaganzas

It has been said that the circus is the only really mysterious thing left in civilization. Here in Spangleland, performers from around the globe astound audiences with a star-dusted repertoire of seemingly impossible feats. Clowns in comical makeup leap out of unexpected places, and magnificent beasts respond as if by magic to the trainer's command.

The circus can be traced back to the Roman amphitheater, although these ancient spectacles featured mostly chariot races and gladiator fights. In the Middle Ages, wandering tumblers, jugglers, acrobats, and animal trainers performed wherever people gathered.

The circus as we know it did not appear until 1768, when a trick rider found that if he galloped in a circle while standing on his horse's back, centrifugal force helped him keep his balance. From then on, organized circus performances were held in rings, usually in permanent or semipermanent buildings.

The big top originated in the 1820's. At first, circus tents were small, housing a single ring and several hundred portable seats. A few decades later, big tops rivaled the ancient hippodromes in magnitude, covering up two acres with 11 tons of canvas.

By the 1870's, American circuses were glittering extravaganzas, carried from town to town by dozens of railroad cars. Generations of families made the circus their life and livelihood. A special language evolved, mingling foreign tongues, thieves' argot, and terms used to describe objects and locations peculiar to the circus.

In circus lingo, a *sucker* is a circus-goer, an *Annie Oakley* is a ticket, and a *Bible* is a program or magazine. *Lot loafers* or *lotlice* are townspeople who hang around the lot. The *back yard* is the space between the big top and the dressing rooms, where wardrobes and props are stored. The *white wagon* is the main office on the circus lot. The *blues* are the cheapest seats in the big top. *Side-walling* - crawling in under the canvas wall - is the last resource of local urchins who can even afford the blues.

Illegal gambling is called *grift*. "*Hey Rube*!" is the rallying cry for help in a fight between circus people and toughs or irate townspeople. A *Monday Man* was permitted to steal from village clotheslines. A *Johnny Tin Plate* is a small town marshall or constable, a *First of May* is a novice performer, and a *roustabout* is a common laborer. Extra work is called *cherry pie*. A *keister* is a trunk or wardrobe box. A clown is a *Joey*. And *clown alley* is a dressing tent or trailer reserved exclusively for clowns.

As the circus parade with its gaudy wagons, proud tigers, and whistling calliope rolls through town, who among us does not feel a thrill of excitement? For we know that when the great tent is erected and the Joeys leave clown alley for the performance ring, we can all join in on the magic and mystery of the circus.

RIMSHAW
THE
INCOMPARABLE

# Divines the Future, Resurrects the Past!

RIMSHAW

From the mysterious mountains of Eastern Europe, we bring you RIMSHAW THE EMCOMPARABLE, augur of the future, interpreter of the past, diviner of hidden attributes.

Born of humble parents on the fog-shrouded coast of Cornwall, England, Rodney Rimshaw astonished the world at the age of two by foretelling an assassination attempt against the visiting Czar of Bulgaria. The grateful monarch invited little Rodney and his family to join him at his spacious palace in the Bulgarian highlands. There Rimshaw was taken on as apprentice to the court astrologer, whence he learned to command the movements of the planets and stars and discern the hidden magnetic forces that control the destiny of every living creature. As seer for the Czar, young Rodney assisted in the machinations of the throne until 1943, when the monarch, ignoring Rimshaw's warnings, made an ill-fated voyage to Berlin. Grieving Bulgarians blamed Rimshaw for failing to prevent the journey, and the slandered soothsayer was forced to flee across the border to Yugoslavia. It was there Tomas Munrab found him, forty years later, plying his mystic skills in a hut outside the mountain village of Strup.

Today we are fortunate to have access to the same skills that once influenced a great Balkan nation. By placing his subject under hypnosis. Rimshaw is able to recall the past in astounding detail. By tracing the distinctive lines of the palm, he is able to foretell the roads that lie ahead. And by kneading the bumps on one's head, he is able to determine individual traits and talents and how they may best be applied.

Hypnotist, phrenologist, palmist, mystic beyond - RIMSHAW THE INCOMPARABLE.

Half Man/
Half Woman

Believe It
or Not!

827
Pounds
of
Feminine
Charm

In the world of physical phenomenon, few genetic oddities can compete with the strange union of a man and a woman in one body. It is particularly rare and fascinating to find the figure split, vertically, with one half entirely given over to the male and the other half entirely to the female.

The Traveling Circus That Time Forgot, Inc. is honored to call itself home to Andrew Jenny, a delightful example of this particular biological quirk. Andrew is the epitome of masculine bravado, while Jenny exudes a beguiling femininity.

Guests are received in Jenny's cozy boudoir, where time flies by in the distinguished company of one of nature's most intriguing curiosities.

Imagine giving birth to a 36-pound baby girl! That was the joyful surprise for Mrs. Oscar Whittlesby, statuesque wife of the renowned meteorologist, on New Year's Day 1966 at their home in the Northwest Territories.

This scientific miracle was only the first in a series of fantastic milestones in the life of our alluring Tina. By the age of 8, the tyke weighed in at an astonishing 410 pounds. By age 12, she weighed 639 pounds. And at age 14, when she reached her full adult height of 6'5", Tina tipped the scales at a truly monumental 827 pounds, over a third of a ton!

Like the pleasingly plump maidens in paintings of yore, Tina retains a winsome charm and a fashionable flair much appreciated by her fellow performers. Stop by her tent and say hello to the largest enchantress in the world!

## DR. NOSTRUM'S EXTRACT

This medicine was originated by Dr. Nostrum in 1863 and since that time numbers of grateful patients have testified to its worth. It should be in every medicine cabinet as it is a prompt and pleasant remedy for aches, pains, sour stomach, heartburn, sick headache, constipation, diarrhea, biliousness, itch, "singer's throat," and pin worms.

Dr. Nostrum's contains 19% alcohol as a preservative and solvent.

**For Toothache—**Wet cotton with Dr. Nostrum's Extract and crowd into the cavity, or lay it around the roots of the aching tooth; also bathe the face over the tooth with Dr. Nostrum's.

**For Itch—**Lie on flannel wet with Dr. Nostrum's Extract.

**For Grippe & Catarrh—**Take two teaspoonfuls of Dr. Nostrum's Extract three times a day. Apply Dr. Nostrum's to all sore spots. Sleep indoors, preferably in bed, until the attack is broken.

**For Constipation, Diarrhea & Related Difficulties—**One teaspoonful of Dr. Nostrum's Extract three times a day, to be taken half an hour before meals. Eat simple food and then only when hungry. Take outdoor exercise, be regular in habits, and drink plenty of water.

**Sick Headache—**Headache is often due to indigestion. Keep as quiet as possible, clean out the intestinal canal with Dr. Nostrum's Extract, eat slow, and chew the food well.

**For Sore Throat—**Put a piece of flannel around the throat wet with Dr. Nostrum's Extract. Do not leave on too long or blistering may occur.

**For Pin Worms—**Round and pin worms are transmitted to the human body as Worm Eggs, swallowed in water, or in uncooked meat and vegetables. Treat with four tablespoons of Dr. Nostrum's Extract six times a day. Dr. Nostrum's paralyzes the worm and makes it let go its hold.

# Infidel

Preface to the Story

You like to think of yourself as a bold and adventurous soldier of fortune, daring to brave the perils of the Egyptian Desert in search of a great lost pyramid. In fact, you're a small-time explorer, and you've just been marooned by your crew. Thoughts of getting lost, starving to death, or dying of thirst cross your mind, but you are sustained by the faint hope that you can somehow find the pyramid in this smoldering heat. You're all alone. Perhaps the sun has affected your thinking. Do you really expect to find a lost pyramid in this vast, endless desert, much less survive? Even if you do find it, can you get inside? Hardest of all, are you capable of matching wits with the ancient Egyptians? Still, you're driven onward against desperate odds. Undreamed-of riches and treasures beyond imagination await you. And your pride and dignity, your reputation and self-esteem, are at stake.

For you are branded INFIDEL.

About the Author

Michael Berlyn is a writer whose books include The Integrated Man and Crystal Phoenix from Bantam Books. He is the author of SUSPENDED, INFIDEL, and CUTTHROATS, all from Infocom.

**AIR EL MENHIR**

**Boarding Pass**

FLIGHT•
976Y

DATE OF FLIGHT•
JULY 9

GATE•
23

DESTINATION•
EL MENHIR-EGYPT

BOARDING TIME•
3 PM

DEPARTURE TIME•
3:25 PM

SEAT NUMBER•
13B AISLE
NON-SMOKING

CLASS•
COACH

TICKET NUMBER•
0098 764 9823

ESTIMATED TIME OF ARRIVAL•
2:30 PM JULY 10

July 8

I think I'm on to something big. Really big. This is the chance I've been waiting for, the chance to prove to everyone that I'm not just someone's errand boy.

After the way Craige treated me on that ridiculous safari, I developed a distaste for him. Everyone jumped when he spoke — the great white hunter, puffed up and dressed the part. I knew everything he knew about running a safari and he still treated me like dirt. Even his client, Joshua Rankin, thought Craige was someone really special, someone who had seen everything, been everywhere, was always in control of every situation.

The way he always barked orders got to me after a while. "Help the bearers strike the tents," he'd say, or, "Check the supplies." God, how I learned to despise him. I played it smart, though. I knew better than to confront him, to let him know I saw right through him. I bided my time, waited till we were back in the States, then formulated a simple plan. It was risky, and I had no idea what Craige would do if he caught me at it, but I was just as good as him, and all I needed was the break to prove it.

Well that break came this morning, when a Miss Ellingsworth called. Craige was out of the office, so I answered the phone. I told a little lie when I told her who I was. She wanted someone with a lot of experience to find something out in the desert, and I told her I was Craige's partner, and I had all the experience for the job. When she asked for Craige, who was out checking on some new equipment, I told her he was on safari, and it was me or no one.

She bit! She gave me her address and I went over to talk to her. She was a gray-haired spinster type, about 65 or so, living in an old, pretty run-down place. This is the story she told me:

Her father was an archaeologist in the early part of the century. Somehow he got his hands on an ancient artifact, a pottery shard more than 5000 years old inscribed with strange hieroglyphs. From what he deciphered, the shard pointed to the general location of a pyramid, a pyramid which no one had ever heard of before. He kept as quiet about his discovery as possible and, after four years of bowing, scraping, and petitioning foundations and universities, managed to fund a small expedition in 1920. He took his wife and newborn daughter along for the trip. After a few months of disheartening searching, he came across something which proved he was on the right track — a small block of limestone inscribed with those same odd hieroglyphs. When he decoded it he discovered it referred to vast riches and a queen.

That's as far as he got, though. The desert heat and the local water got to him and he died there.

His widow and child returned to the States and, when Tut's tomb was discovered a few years later, Miss Ellingsworth's mother figured they'd dug up her dead husband's pyramid. She stowed all his records and belongings in a steamer chest and forgot about the whole thing.

And there it rested for sixty years until the mother died. Miss Ellingsworth went through the stuff in the attic and found the limestone cube, a map, a partial hieroglyphic dictionary, and a rubbing of the cube. From what she could tell, the pyramid was nowhere near Tut's, so she called Craige to see what could be done.

"Just think of the historical significance of such a discovery," Miss Ellingsworth said to me, handing over her father's things. Sure, it was a cinch. I looked the pieces over. With the map, the task seemed easy. I could practically see the pyramid in my mind. All the glory would be mine — not Craige's! This was a chance to show the world what a fool Craige was, a chance to prove that I was better than him. There would be enough gold and treasures in the pyramid to set me up for life but, more importantly, it would give me the reputation I deserved but had been denied by the glory-grabbing Craige.

I've been preparing for something like this to come along. I've saved money, sold the condo and just about everything I had that was worth anything, waiting patiently for the right opportunity. Now it's here and I realize I'm under-capitalized.

Miss Ellingsworth has no money — all she really wants out of this is to make her Dad into someone famous — so it's all up to me.

I packed my bags and got my visa today. Tomorrow I take off for Egypt. I won't bother giving Craige notice.

JULY 13

We leave for the pyramid site tomorrow at daybreak. I'm in El Menhir, a muddy little village on the Nile. I've managed to keep my purpose here a secret — I told the locals I was a scientist, interested in making sonar soundings in the desert. But I did confide in Abdul, the top guide in the area. He'll be the go-between for me and the locals he lined up to do the work. He also rounded up all the supplies we need — tents, K-rations, cooking utensils, and the like.

July 22

It's been one disaster after another, but none of it is <u>really</u> my fault! First, we hardly get into the real desert area when the navigation box falls off the back of the jeep. Great! I had to radio back to Cairo

for a replacement and they said they'd get it to me,
air-drop it into the encampment, in a few days—
another expense in an already tight expedition $$$!!

Then the dates Abdul bought turned out to be insect infested and spoiled. The locals started grumbling and muttering, and one of them had the nerve to demand more money!

I promised everyone a big bonus if all went well.

They looked at me as if I were lying. I don't think they trust me, and I don't know how much longer I can keep them digging, and still stay in control. I don't remember Craige ever having these problems. And this kind of thing sure never happened to the heroes in "True Tales of Adventure."

AUGUST 6 We've been at the site for three weeks and the new navigation box still hasn't arrived. I figured it would be best to keep the men busy—"idle hands" and all that—digging in the general area indicated on the map. Without that box, though, it's like looking for a needle in a haystack.

Worse, the crew suspects I'm trying to pull a fast one on them. Abdul came to me and said I had better do something or there'd be trouble. I laughed at Abdul, telling him that I was in control, that nothing was going to happen that I didn't want to happen. Abdul said "What about the box? Did you want it to break?"

I guess I got a little too angry when he said that. I slapped him across the face! Abdul said nothing, but he glared at me. I think I might have handled him better.

AUGUST 8 THE BOX STILL ISN'T HERE! Without it, I don't think I'll be able to hold things together much longer. Our food stores are pretty low. The men are grumbling more and more. They stop working unless I stand over them and watch. One of them simply refuses to work at all, and Abdul is no real help. He seems to take their side.

August 12

No box!! Radioed Cairo yesterday and the day before. They assure me it's on the way. If it is, then where is it?

Abdul led the men into the desert to perform some religious ceremony, but I didn't believe it was a holy day. All I could think was that the whole thing was getting out of control. That I was losing the only real chance I ever had. That if I didn't get them back to digging, it would be all over.

I marched out into the desert to confront Abdul. I asked him to stop this foolishness and get back to work. Abdul looked very offended! I pushed him, demanding he order the men to work. He didn't push me back, but he did say, "You shall regret that, sacrilegious dog!"

Terrific! Looks like I blew it. How was I to know it really was a holiday? They moved off further into the desert to conduct their ceremony out of my sight. A little later, while I was lying on my cot, trying to figure out what to say to them that wouldn't sound too much like an apology, one of the men came into my tent. He seemed real friendly, and asked for the calfskin of kumiss. I figured they'd gotten over my little flareup and all was forgiven.

He brought the calfskin back a few minutes ago. I'm going to write to Miss Ellingsworth back in the States to assure her everything's going okay. One thing I don't need is for her to hire someone else for this job, especially after what I've been through. A few swigs of kumiss should get me through the letter OK.

IOU's

Sally $400
Abdul L£25
Kahmir L£12 plus tip!
Mom ~~$28~~ $48 plus 5% interest
Joyce $50 plus dinner

Air Mail

Rose Ellingsworth
55 Wheeler Street
Cambridge, MA 02138
USA

HOTEL AMÉRICAIN

Abbâs Hilmil Blvd. El Menhir, Egypt 8-6130-5 Cable: HASKELLOTELS

August 12

Dear Rose,

Here we are at the site, the same site that your father's expedition occupied almost 65 years ago, and things could hardly be any better. The weather is about average for the season — it'd be about 105° in the shade, if there were any shade — and aside from the occasional sandstorms, our camp has remained a merry one. Abdul and the boys are having a wonderful time, and we're all hitting it off just fine.

I guess it's true what they say about us all being brothers under the skin. Notwithstanding the archaeological importance of the find and the profits it may accrue, the greatest treasure I'll bring back from this journey is the wealth of understanding I've gained through our brisk cultural exchange of customs and ideas. The other night, for instance, I treated the fellows to their first omelettes, and you should have heard the exclamations with which they greeted this new culinary experience. For my part, I'm rapidly acquiring a taste for kumiss, a refreshing native beverage made from fermented camel's milk. At first the flavor seemed strange to my western palate, but of late I've grown exceedingly familiar with it. In fact, I'm enjoying a stoup of kumiss right now. I shall be sure to bring you a bottle or two of this zesty concoction upon my return.

Of course everything can't be perfect. We've had a slight delay while we wait for the new navigation box to arrive. (I may have forgotten to mention in my previous letter that the old box became damaged just as we were setting out.) Nevertheless, such is the spirit of camaraderie and good fellowship here in camp that the boys voluntarily continued digging on the off chance that we might locate the pyramid without the aid of scientific instrumentation. This steadfastness in the face of adversity is truly heartwarming and I've rewarded the crew by giving them today off.

This has given me a chance to get off by myself and relax. The strain of command must be telling on me — just now, as I was sipping some kumiss, I began to feel lightheaded, and my knees buckled slightly. Or perhaps I'm just intoxicated with the awe-inspiring vastness of this solitude that surrounds me. In any case, I shall have to lay this letter aside for the time being, until this numbness leaves my hands and the landscape stops writhing around so violently... Hello I ~~hat~~ have been staring at the same grain of sand

for last hour and have you ever heard it said
that if you move one grain of sand you
Change the course of history? well here goes nothing—
There, I done it, hope I've made the world a better
place to live in..... My my ~~doesn't~~ don't I feel strange
tonight I wonder what's come over me but wait!!!!
there was something very important I meant to
tell you about this waistland Oh yes now I remember
Did you ever stop to think that T.S. Eliot's name
is an anagram for "toilets"? I think I now
understand what he was trying to tell us all,
Rosetta——————
must be the desertsuns played
mischeff with my eyes for now as i gaze across

the moonlit dunes who are in no way related
to lorna dune i see theyve turned into crashing
curling waves in an endless sea to shining
sea how they cast strange shadowshapes of wild
arabian demons who are coming for me
with my final summons in the kitchen with dinah so
possibly its the kumiss thats causing these tiny
little spots to dance and swirl before my
eyes like granes of sand through an hourglass
so are the daze of our life savings blown
on a hopeless expidision thats gonna get
yors trully killed just so i can watch these
spots as they grow and grow and get funnier an funnier

until theyre changed into gnarled blue men
about two foot tall with evilgrins behind their
twisting bristly green wiskers that hang all the way
to their skinnyshinshins as the three little pigs
used to say in piglatin eeway eeway eeway all the
way home home on the range
where there's no place like home
place like home is where the heartbreak of psoriasis there's no
is that A shadow i see moving or cood
it be abdul returning cood it be mack the
knife cood it be desert sickness what cood it be

this cotton mouthed icysweating brainfeverish
rubberarms and legs and head for the hills
are alive with the sound of musicker and
sicker may be its something i ate guess
i shouldve left that last deviledhammeatball alone

Hieroglyphic cube
found 27 September 1920

Cube measured 4" x 4" x 4"
with hieroglyphics legible one side.
Composition Nummulitic limestone.

Hieroglyphics on cube
match the symbols from
pottery shard.
Deciphered symbols
support the "Lost Pyramid"
hypothesis.

| HIEROGLYPHIC SYMBOL | ENGLISH TRANS. |
|---|---|
| # | the |
| #: | this |
| :: | and |
| (( )) | all |
| !@! | queen |
| — | sit/lies/rests |
| / | to/toward |
| → | through |
| ⊓ | entrance/door |
| // \\ | treasures |

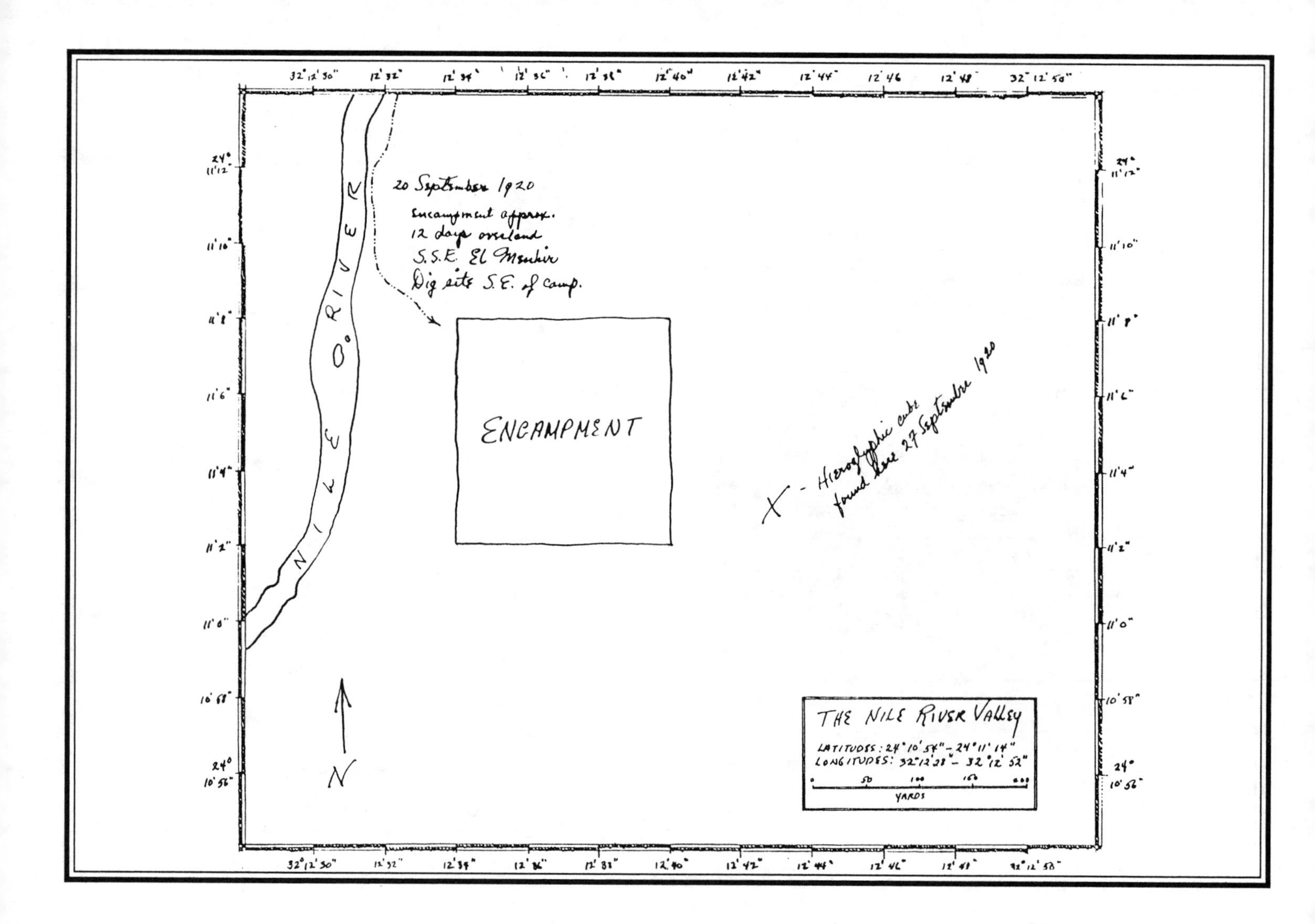
20 September 1920
Encampment approx.
12 days overland
S.S.E. El Menkir
Dig site S.E. of camp.
NILE RIVER
ENCAMPMENT
X - Hieroglyphic cube
found here 27 Septembre 1920
N
THE NILE RIVER VALLEY
LATITUDES: 24° 10' 54" - 24° 11' 14"
LONGITUDES: 32° 12' 28" - 32° 12' 52"
0 50 100 150 200
YARDS

# Moonmist

Preface to the Story

In Moonmist, you are a famous young American detective. An old friend, Tamara Lynd, has written you a letter, asking for your help. And so you have travelled to England to test your detective skills. As the story begins, you are outside Tresyllian Castle — the old, dark, hauntingly beautiful castle where Tamara now lives. Tamara greets you, and you meet some interesting guests. But your visit soon turns to mystery, as a trail of riddles and clues leads you to a hidden valuable treasure. But Tamara is worried about a ghost that is tormenting her. What does the ghost want? Is it jealous of her? Does the ghost want the hidden treasure for itself? Or is the ghost a fake — just someone dressing up to frighten Tamara? If so, why? These mysteries and others are waiting to test your wits in Moonmist.

About the Authors

Stu Galley was a student of physics and journalism when he discovered computers, which at the time were mostly just big number-crunchers. At first he thought computers were too much fun to be taken seriously, until he decided that physics was too little fun to be taken seriously. At MIT he discovered computer games and LISP-like languages and met the other founders of Infocom. He began writing interactive fiction in 1982 and has authored The Witness, Seastalker, and Moonmist, all for Infocom.

Jim Lawrence has written fiction extensively for both children and adults in a variety of media: books, magazine articles, film and radio scripts, and comic strips, including "decision" strips. He estimates that he has written some sixty books of fiction, many of them under pen names for series like Tom Swift Jr. and Nancy Drew. His radio credits include weekly scripts for Sergeant Preston of the Yukon, The Green Hornet, and Sky King. He has written for, and in some cases created and illustrated, the comic strips Dallas, Joe Palooka, Captain Easy, Friday Foster, and Buck Rogers. To date, he has authored two works of interactive fiction published by Infocom: Seastalker, published in 1984, and Moonmist, in 1986.

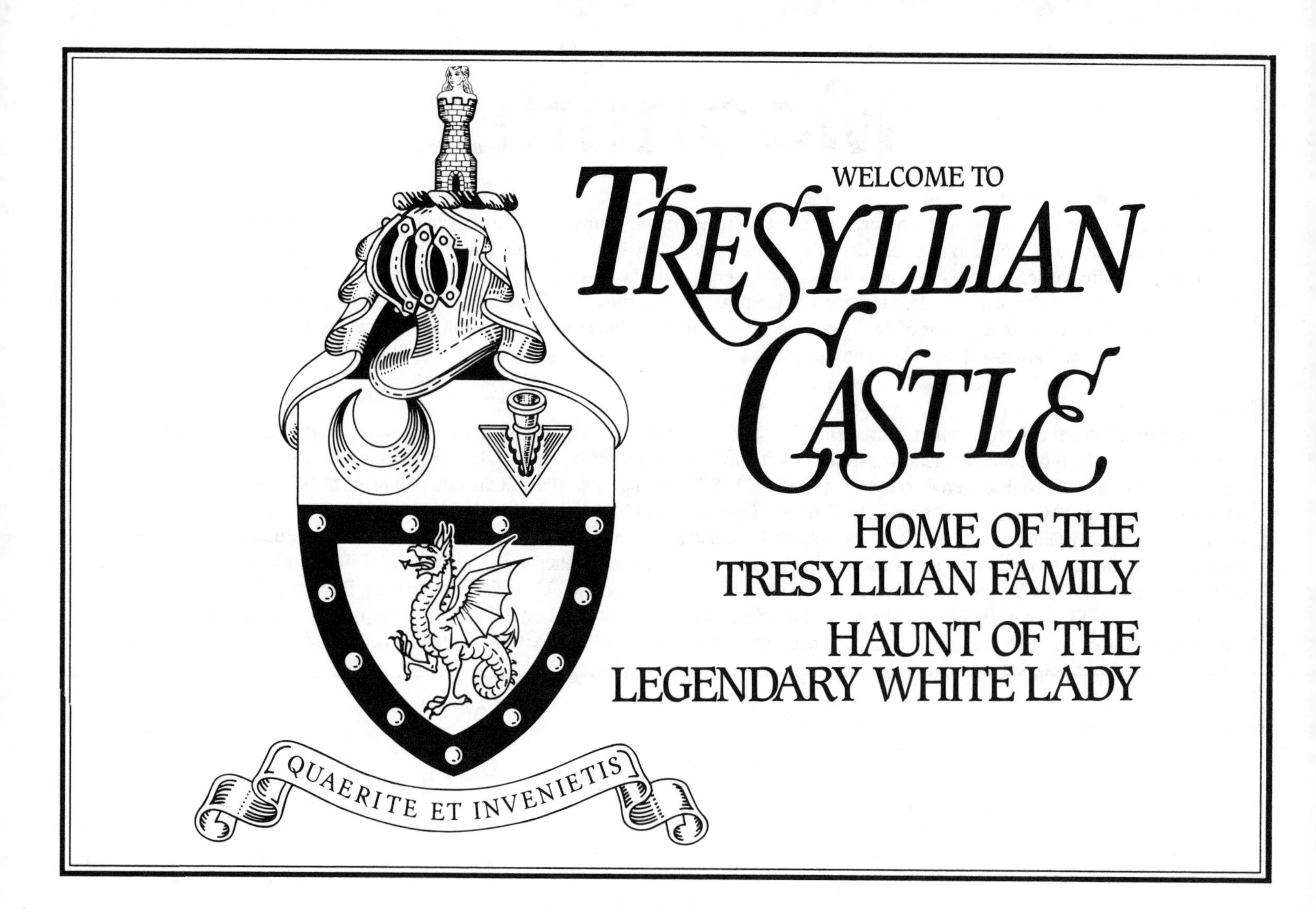
WELCOME TO
TRESYLLIAN
CASTLE
HOME OF THE
TRESYLLIAN FAMILY
HAUNT OF THE
LEGENDARY WHITE LADY
QUAERITE ET INVENIETIS

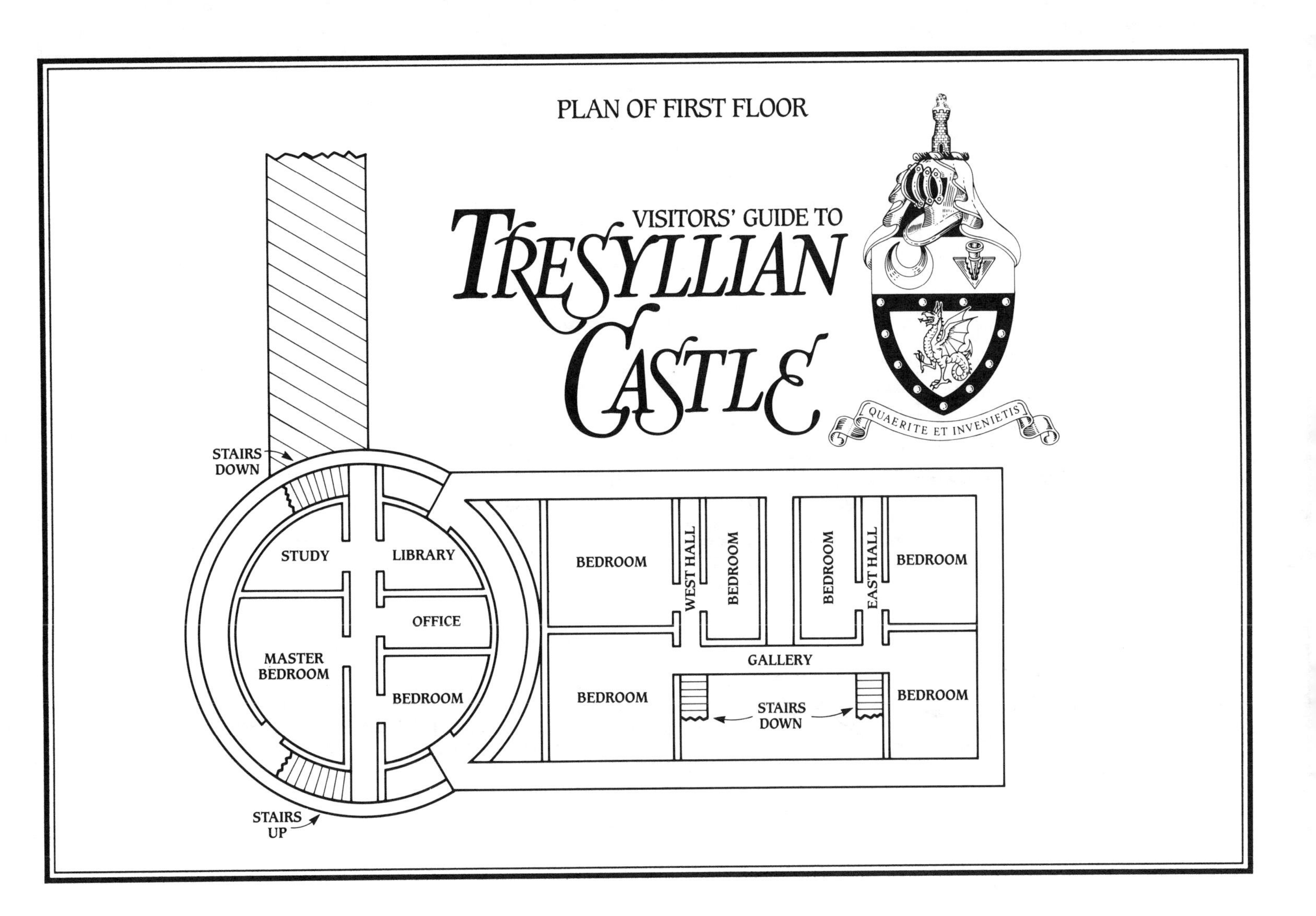
PLAN OF FIRST FLOOR
VISITORS' GUIDE TO
TRESYLLIAN CASTLE
QUAERITE ET INVENIETIS
STAIRS DOWN
STUDY
LIBRARY
OFFICE
MASTER BEDROOM
BEDROOM
STAIRS UP
BEDROOM
WEST HALL
BEDROOM
BEDROOM
EAST HALL
BEDROOM
GALLERY
BEDROOM
STAIRS DOWN
BEDROOM

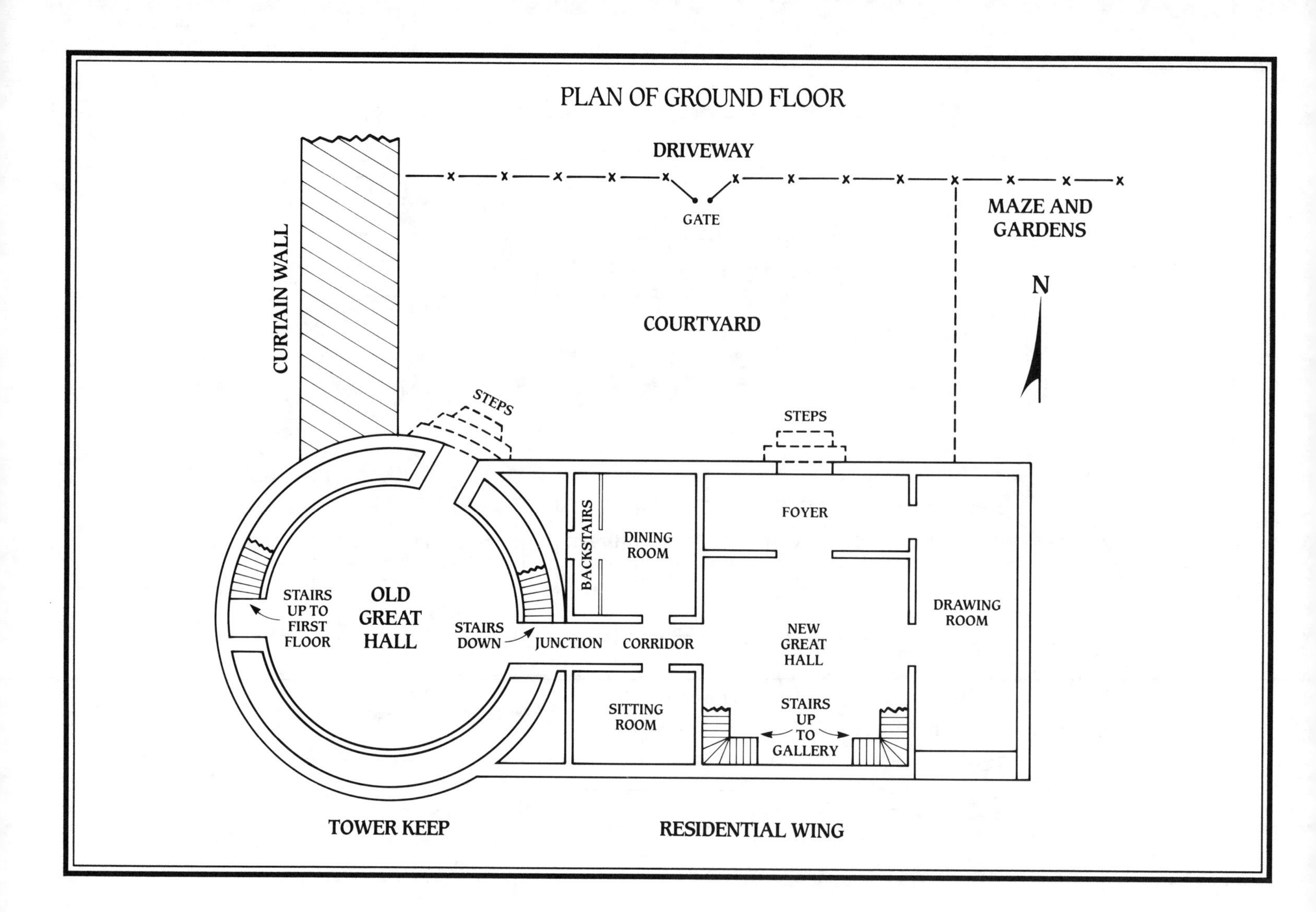
PLAN OF GROUND FLOOR
DRIVEWAY
GATE
MAZE AND GARDENS
CURTAIN WALL
COURTYARD
N
STEPS
STEPS
FOYER
BACKSTAIRS
DINING ROOM
STAIRS UP TO FIRST FLOOR
OLD GREAT HALL
STAIRS DOWN
JUNCTION
CORRIDOR
NEW GREAT HALL
DRAWING ROOM
SITTING ROOM
STAIRS UP TO GALLERY
TOWER KEEP
RESIDENTIAL WING

he best way to approach Cornwall is from the sea, as the first traders did thousands of years ago. Mediterranean travellers, rounding Gibraltar and sailing north along the coast, find a peninsula shaped like a miniature Italy, tipped on its side and projecting from the southwest corner of England into the Atlantic waters.

It is in Cornwall that King Arthur held court, at a spot now known as Camelford. Across these moors rode Galahad and Lancelot. On these shores Iseult pined for her lost love, Tristram. And on these mighty cliffs Jack killed the giants Cormoran, Galligantus, and Thunderbore.

Many Cornish folk believe in fairies, wishes, charms, and omens. And why not? In Cornwall, such things do exist. Gnomes hammer away in the tin mines. Pixies turn the milk sour. When a pin is thrown into the Holy Well near Roche on Maundy Thursday, the bubbles reveal your fortune. A ghost coach drawn by headless horses appears in Penryn just before Christmas. If you don't avert your eyes when you see it, the coachman will spirit you away.

Cornwall has many interesting old manor houses, a number of them built in the Middle Ages. There are also several castles, mostly in ruins but still impressive. These ancient dwellings have housed distinguished Cornish families and witnessed countless historical events. Tresyllian Castle, a mediaeval fortress with a residential wing attached, is a fine example of such a home.

The oldest parts of the castle, the Tower and the Curtain Wall, were built in 1242 by Horace of Tresyllian, to defend Frobzance Cove from pirates at sea. In 1251, Horace constructed a Chapel (uniquely situated on the second floor of the Tower) for the baptism of his first son and heir.

Tresyllian Castle has its share of Cornish lore. The legend of the White Lady originated in the 14th century, when Sir Thomas Tresyllian's young bride proved unfaithful and was walled up alive as punishment. Her woeful spirit wanders the Tower on moonlit nights.

Tresyllian Castle was renovated in the mid 1500's, when Francis Tattersall-Tresyllian, 11th Earl of Frobzance, 3rd Baron Tatdale, built a Residential Wing on the site of the eastern part of the original Curtain Wall. The rooms were refurbished in 1867 in anticipation of a visit from Queen Victoria.

Situated on Frobzance Cove, with a commanding view of the English Channel, the castle is a charming blend of historical treasures and everyday comforts, carefully maintained for our enjoyment by the noble Tresyllian family.

TRESYLLIAN CASTLE IS ALMOST EIGHT CENTURIES OLD. AFTER ALL THESE YEARS, IT IS STILL INHABITED BY MEMBERS OF THE TRESYLLIAN FAMILY.

Imagine yourself as an eighteenth-century traveller, riding your horse across the desolate Cornish moors. Throughout the long day, you see nothing but scrub and bog and craggy rocks looming on the horizon. Toward evening, a dank fog rolls in off the coast. Just as you're contemplating the terrors of spending a night on the moor, the stone turrets of a castle appear through the mist. A flag bearing a noble coat of arms flutters from the tower. As you ride closer, light blazes from the mullioned windows and a servant runs out to take your weary steed. You have arrived at Tresyllian Castle.

Today, Lord Tresyllian offers thousands of yearly visitors the same hospitality family friends have been accorded through the centuries. When viewing the castle, it is easy to picture oneself as the historic traveller, arriving at last at a civilised place.

## The Courtyard

The stones which pave the Courtyard bear the marks of centuries of revelry, warfare, and everyday life. The crumbling Curtain Wall southwest of the gate once surrounded the castle, guarding against invaders. The Tower (also called the Keep) provided living space. During the frequent battles, mediaeval maidens huddling in barren rooms could hear the shouts of the marauders and the thud of the battering ram against the massive wooden door.

Now a luxurious Residential Wing has replaced the eastern section of the Wall, and the only sounds you hear are the surging surf in the nearby cove and the welcoming voice of your host.

## The Foyer

The decor of the austere, high-ceilinged Foyer reflects the Tresyllian family's pride in their Cornish heritage. Footsteps echo on the granite paving stones, carved from the Cornish hills. The huge sculpted bronze doors leading into the Great Hall tell the tale of Tristram and Iseult, unhappy bride of the King of Cornwall. And the oil painting near the mahogany coat rack shows Jack the Giant Killer, another famous resident of Cornwall, slaying the two-headed giant Thunderbore.

The umbrella stand by the front door is actually an elephant's foot. When the eccentric Lord Chester Tresyllian was on safari in 1902, a large bull elephant trampled the campsite, breaking his Lordship's foot. In revenge, Lord Chester shot the elephant and brought back *its* foot to hold his umbrellas.

## The Drawing Room

The airy Drawing Room is where the Tresyllian family meets to enjoy each other's company as well as that of their guests. The Dresden blue walls and furnishings soothe the senses and complement the elegant gold-leafed frames around the many mirrors and paintings.

The spacious feeling is enhanced by the tall French windows, which overlook Frobzance Cove to the east and the formal gardens to the north. The Belgian tapestry on the south wall is a treasured family heirloom. Woven of wool and spun gold, it depicts a maiden tending a unicorn in a beautiful rose garden.

The satin cushion of the small gold-leafed armchair before the fireplace bears the imprint of Queen Victoria, for this is where she sat on her visit to Tresyllian Castle in 1867.

## The New Great Hall

In the Middle Ages, entire families lived and slept in a castle's great hall. By the time the Tresyllian Family built their New Great Hall, the room was used mostly for holiday entertaining and for conducting important business.

When the local villagers arrive for Christmas dinner, they are seated around the long oak table in the centre of the room. A fire is lit in the massive fireplace, which is decorated with the Tresyllian coat of arms. The elaborate wood carving surrounding the fireplace extends upward through a vast open stairwell to the gallery, where the portraits of Tresyllian ancestors gaze down upon the festivities.

The suit of armour standing by the bronze doors was worn by Sir Geoffrey Tresyllian at Bosworth Field in 1485. You might think that a knight wearing this armour would feel protected. However, the metal is so heavy that even a strong man had difficulty walking, and fighting an enemy or riding a horse was nearly impossible.

## The Gallery

The Gallery is reached by climbing one of the staircases on either side of the fireplace.

The walls of the Gallery display the Tresyllian family portraits. Among the somber faces of knights and peers, a lighter note is struck by the charming double portrait of Hadley and Zoe Tattersall-Tresyllian by the sixteenth century Austrian painter Baron Roland von Langosy.

High above the fireplace on the south wall, a Gothic window offers a dramatic view of the English Channel, with cargo and pleasure boats plying the blue-grey waters.

## The Sitting Room

The Sitting Room is a delightful place to spend an idle afternoon. It is filled with warm colors and invitingly comfortable furniture. The yellow silk brocade has covered the walls for over a hundred years, and the faded carpet patterned with peacocks and chrysanthemums was purchased in India by Lady Gayle Tresyllian in 1912.

A guest at the castle might write a letter at the Louis XV writing desk that once belonged to Marie Antoinette. Or play a romantic melody on the grand piano especially built by the Klugenhofer Klavierwerke in Germany. Or curl up with a book on the window seat, charmingly decorated with small carved wyverns projecting like gargoyles from either end.

## The Dining Room

In the Dining Room, the Tresyllians and their intimate guests gather to sample the culinary masterpieces of the family cook. It is easy to imagine the servants waiting in attendance as the family settles into the leather-cushioned chairs around the gleaming mahogany table. The matching sideboard can hold an impressive array of food, along with a silver punchbowl on festive occasions.

The room was designed to provide a peaceful and relaxing place to dine. The walls are covered in pale lilac, decorated with plaster friezes of cupids at play. Above the fireplace is a large oil painting of fruits and flowers. The bracketed shelf on the south wall holds a collection of porcelain vases, as well as a bronze bust of Lord Lionel Tresyllian.

## Junction

This is where the Residential Wing joins the old part of the castle. Here you can easily see the double outer wall of the Tower, designed to strengthen the castle against attackers. If invaders did manage to break in, they would have to fight their way up a winding stairway between the two walls, then cross to the opposite side of the Tower in order to reach the next stairway.

Winding stairways take up some of the space between the walls. Legends tell of secret passage-ways in other parts of the Tower.

## The Old Great Hall

Centuries ago, the Old Great Hall was a dark and gloomy place, heated by a smoking fire in a vast stone fireplace and lit by small narrow windows. The only furnishings were a large oak table, a few benches, and a pair of armchairs for the Lord and Lady.

Today, the Old Great Hall looks very much the same. The rough plaster walls are empty of decoration, and light still filters in through the slit windows. The main difference is that the original furniture has been moved to the New Great Hall. In its place, Lord Lionel Tresyllian has set up a collection of mementoes from his travels to the far corners of the globe. Among these curiosities, be sure to look at the following:

✣ **An oil painting of the Battle of Blood River** *by the famous half-Zulu, half-Afrikaner artist, Chaka Pretorius. In this battle, a few hundred Boer settlers circled their wagons on the banks of the Ncome River to defend themselves against an army of Zulu warriors brandishing spears and clubs. Earlier, friends and relatives of these settlers had been slaughtered in a gruesome massacre. The present band, confronted now by overwhelming odds, might well have suffered the same fate. Instead, on Sunday the 16th December 1838, they fought off their attackers, totally defeating the army of the dreaded Zulu king known as Dingaan the Vulture. More than three thousand of his highly trained warriors were killed, whilst only three settlers were wounded. The river ran red, giving the battle its name.*

✣ **An exquisite carving in Chinese jade** *of a rather ape-like, pre-human skeleton, probably some ancestor of modern man.*

✣ **A giant oyster shell** *from the South Pacific ocean, its interior surface mysteriously lacquered jet black.*

✣ **A papier-mache figure of an Amazon Indian,** *dressed in the weird costume of a tribal witch doctor, performing the elaborate secret ritual by which the anaesthetic drug used on the tribal blowgun darts is extracted from the rare moonflower plant.*

## The Hedge Maze

In 1862, the children of Jonathan Tresyllian, 21st Earl of Frobzance, pleaded with their father to let them plan a maze in the garden. The resulting hedge maze is one of the best-known in England. Today, young people (as well as old) still enjoy wandering through the clipped passages of the maze. Hidden in the centre is a beautiful salt-air garden with a stone fountain and a pond filled with shimmering goldfish.

## THE HAUNTED ORCHARD OF PENZANCE

There stands today, in the town of Penzance, a mansion which once belonged to an elderly woman named Mrs. Baines. Old Mrs. Baines took pride in her home and in the fine apple trees in her orchard, whose fruit was well-liked by the local lads. But as time went by, pride soured into avarice, and she set her servant to guarding the orchard by night. This he did, spending long dark hours in the damp grass beneath the trees.

Old Mrs. Baines, trusting no one, feared that her man was not doing his proper job. One night she crept into the garden, dressed in her dark silk mantle. Round the orchard she went, confirming her suspicions: the servant was nowhere in sight. Thinking to teach him a lesson, she climbed into an apple tree and shook down a quantity of apples for the laggard to find scattered upon his return.

Alas, she had misjudged her man. He was not absent, but merely asleep beneath a far tree. Hearing the apples thud to the ground, he leapt to his feet and discharged his gun at the suspected thief. "I'm murdered!" screeched Mrs. Baines, tumbling down amidst the fruit. And indeed she never recovered from her injuries, expiring shortly thereafter.

From then on, the estate has been guarded by the ghost of old Mrs. Baines. In the evenings, she glides amongst the trees, her silk mantle floating in the mist. At times she flies up from the unkempt grass like a dry leaf caught in the wind, perching on the garden wall with her skinny legs protruding from under her skirts. And when darkness falls, a shadowy form peers from a window of the deserted mansion, shaking a threatening fist at passers-by.

No one dares enter the house or orchard, and the apples lie rotting on the ground.

# THE SILKEN SHAWL

A sea captain's wife, yearning to see the world beyond her country village, begged her husband to let her accompany him on his journeys. "My dear wife," said he, "the sea is no place for a lady." But as time went on and she pleaded all the more, he at last agreed that she might voyage with him to the Orient.

The sea was rough, and the journey long and tedious, but the captain's wife found each new day as full of adventure as the last. She loved the deep green sea dipping and swelling on the vast horizon, the clouds scudding overhead in endless variations, and the seabirds swooping low to catch the silvery fish. She loved watching the men high up on the rigging and listening to the sailors' songs at night. And she loved the twisting streets and mysterious bazaars of the Orient, where her husband purchased tea, china, and silk for the London shops.

In one such bazaar, an alleyway of rough stalls overflowing with lustrous garments, the captain bought his wife a gift, a remembrance of their journey. And what a gift it was: a splendid silken shawl, patterned with multicolored songbirds and flowering quince trees, and shot through with fine gold threads. The captain's wife had never seen anything more beautiful in her life, and from then on it was always around her shoulders.

They travelled home around the Cape of Good Hope and up the coast of Africa, braving storms and sickness. At long last they reached the waters of the North Atlantic and knew that the beloved coast of England was not far off.

But familiar channels do not always mean safety. The Captain's ship was attacked by the desperate Newlyn fishermen, who had turned to cold-blooded piracy after several seasons of poor fishing. The pirates made their blindfolded victims walk the plank into the sea to drown, sparing neither women nor children. As the Captain's wife began the slow walk to her doom, one of the blackguards snatched the silken shawl from around her shoulders. And thus was her treasure stolen from her in the last moments of her life.

The pirate took the shawl home to his wife, saying nothing of how he came by it. Dressing for church that Sunday, she put on the silken garment, turning this way and that before the mirror to admire its rich colors and patterns. Suddenly there appeared in the glass the drowned face of the Captain's wife gazing at her over her shoulder. Her wet hair streamed out from her head as though floating in the ocean depths, and her pale hand pointed to the shawl.

The pirate's wife was so horrified that she went raving mad and died shortly thereafter. No one knows what happened to the haunted shawl. It is probably sitting in the drawer of some unsuspecting soul at this very moment.

# THE HAUNTING OF BRISTOL MANOR

In the early part of the eighteenth century, a family emigrated from the city of Bristol to a fertile valley in Cornwall, there to live a life of leisure. The fine home they built was called Bristol Manor.

A cottage was constructed to house the gardener, who lived with his wife and son, a full-grown lad named Erik. It was not long before Erik fell madly in love with the daughter of the manor, a winsome girl with russet hair and laughing eyes who went by the name of Lucy.

But Lucy was pledged to another, a nobleman of wealth and good family. She spurned the lad's advances, little realizing the depth of his feeling. At long last, crazed by bitterness and jealousy, Erik lured the gentle girl to the cottage loft, stealing her maidenhood and flinging her to her death from the upper window. For his crime, he was hunted down and brought to the gallows by the villagers.

From then on, the cottage of Bristol Manor was haunted by the spectres of Erik and Lucy.

The tortured soul of the hanged man preyed on those more fortunate in love than he. Married couples in particular suffered many frightening experiences. Often they awoke at night to a chill wind blowing even in the heat of summer. A feeling of dread would suffuse the room. Candles were suddenly quenched, or flew through the air, flame intact. Lovers found themselves wrenched apart by clammy unseen hands. And a tall figure cloaked in black would sometimes appear, lifting his hood to reveal a death's head.

Single inhabitants of the cottage rarely were bothered, for Lucy's spirit guarded those as yet unwed.

Years passed. The manor house and its cottage fell into disrepair. They lay abandoned for half a century, until at last a nobleman and his wife came to inhabit Bristol Manor. Their youngest son, a boy named Peter, took the gardener's cottage as his playhouse. Despite warnings from the village folk that the site was haunted, he spent much time there and never found cause for distress.

Peter followed the old legends with interest. He felt a special bond with Lucy and imagined that he might have kept her from harm had he only been there on that fateful day. Often he sensed that her spirit was there beside him, as he played, read, or daydreamed in the dusty rooms of the little cottage.

The years went by, and Peter grew into manhood. Soon it was time for him to leave home for the university. He decided to tidy up his childhood refuge before departing, little knowing when he might return. Going to the cottage, he straightened out the meager pieces of furniture and swept the earthen floor. Finally he stepped back to admire his handiwork.

There, in the middle of the just-swept floor, was a delicate gold locket. He picked it up and undid the clasp. Inside was the timeworn image of a winsome girl with russet hair and laughing eyes—a girl by the name of Lucy.

# THE LEGEND OF PENROSE

Ralph Penrose, on the death of his beloved wife, took his seven-year-old son Edmund to sea. Accompanying them was Ralph's best friend and cousin, William Penrose. The family estate in Sennen was left in the care of Ralph's brother John.

One winter's night, Ralph Penrose was nearing home when a gale struck, tossing his ship upon the sea 'til it crashed into the dreaded Cowloe Rock. The men launched a lifeboat, but this too foundered, flinging them all into the frigid water. Flares from the endangered ship had warned the Penrose household, but John, watching from the shore, made no effort to rescue the drowning men. None were known to survive but Edmund, Ralph's young son, heir to the estate.

John appointed himself guardian of the boy and behaved as if the property were his own. To fatten the family coffers, he built a pirate ship and manned it with a bloodthirsty captain and crew. Wild parties were held in the Great Hall at Penrose, and the village folk barred their doors at night for fear of John and his rowdy companions.

At the turn of the year, snow fell in Sennen and wolves were heard howling in the fields. John sent the household out to hunt, himself staying at home with young Edmund, the pirate captain and a bottle of brandy. When the servants returned, Edmund was nowhere in sight. His uncle and the captain, incoherent with drink, indicated that the lad had joined the hunt. A lengthy search of grounds and countryside showed no trace of the boy, and he was finally assumed to have lost his way in the blinding snow and fallen to his death from the cliffs.

The following year, on the anniversary of Edmund's disappearance, a bearded stranger appeared at Penrose Manor, begging for food and shelter. This was a common occurrence in those days, and the tramp was readily admitted and shown to a bedchamber. In the Great Hall, John Penrose and his lawless guests welcomed in the New Year. Upstairs, the stranger stood at his window, gazing out at the wintry night.

All at once, a great wall of silvery fog came rolling in from the coast. Upon the fog came a roaring sound like that of a stormy sea. The sound drew nearer and nearer, and in a moment the sea itself was spilling into the courtyard, bearing on its crest a phantom boat filled with shouting men. The boat overturned, spilling her crew who with pale faces and staring eyes tried in vain to save themselves. At last there was but one man gazing up at the window where the stranger stood and crying out, "William Penrose, arise and avenge the murder of my son!" Then the sea disappeared, the mist dissolved, and all was as it had been.

William Penrose, for indeed the stranger was he, suddenly recalled the crashing ship, the struggle through the cold waters, and the months of wandering the countryside, unknown to himself or any other man, until instinct led him back to Penrose Manor.

Turning from the window, William saw the small, pale spirit of Edmund hovering in the darkened bedchamber. The spirit whispered, "My uncle bade the captain murder me. I lie beneath the dead tree in the orchard. Dig, and you shall find me. Dig, and place my bones in Sennen churchyard. Dig, and give me peace at last."

That night, digging under the bare limbs of an old tree in the orchard, William uncovered the bloodied remains of the little boy. Gently he carried them to Sennen churchyard, where they were given a proper burial. When William returned to Penrose Manor, the body of John Penrose was swaying from a beam in the garden shed. He had hung himself in sight of the unearthed grave under the dead apple tree.

## THE REVEREND DENSHAM

In an isolated part of the Bodmin moor lies the town of Warleggan. To this remote location came the Rev. Densham, newly inducted vicar of the parish church.

It soon transpired that the Reverend was not happy with his flock. He complained about the size of the congregation, which in those lonely parts was small indeed. To increase the fold, he created a number of paperboard images, propping them up in the pews to fill the church on Sundays.

Despite his desire for a full church, Rev. Densham never went into the village or visited his parishioners. He set a large box by his gate, directing that all groceries and mail should be placed within. He surrounded his property with high fences topped with barbed wire. And as if this were not enough, he imported a half-dozen savage dogs to roam the garden, snarling and snapping at whoever might venture into the neighboring lane.

The parishioners appealed to the Bishop, but since the vicar had done nothing to offend religious law, the Church was powerless to remove him. He still conducted the service every Sunday, although by now the cutout figures were his sole congregation, and for this faithful observance he was assumed to be a man of God.

Years passed. The dogs died and the fence fell into decay. Nothing was seen of the Reverend beyond the smoke curling from the rectory chimney and the occasional glimpse of a tall figure in a black stove-pipe hat and frock coat pacing in the garden.

One day the villagers noticed an absence of smoke from the vicar's chimney. Gathering up their courage, they broke into the rectory. There they found rooms furnished with little more than sacks and packing cases, with gaping holes where the floorboards had been torn up to serve as fuel. On the stairs lay the Reverend, as lifeless as his cardboard congregation.

Never again has a vicar come to live in the rectory at Warleggan. But although the old house has found a measure of peace, the Rev. Densham has not. In the evenings, a phantom in a stove-pipe hat still paces the garden, back and forth across the ruins of the lawn, deep in melancholy thought.

# THE WHITE LADY OF TRESYLLIAN CASTLE

Long ago, when pirates roamed the Cornish coast, a maiden came to Tresyllian Castle, pledged to marry Sir Thomas Tresyllian. The bride had the bloom of youth upon her, and her fair hair was worn in a girlhood braid. Her betrothed was a man much her senior in years and experience, who took what he wanted and allowed no room for error on the part of others.

The marriage was not a happy one. The bride spent many months alone in the dreary castle by the sea, awaiting the return of Sir Thomas, off fighting for the King. The parish holds no record of children gracing the household of Thomas Tresyllian, nor of noble banquets held in the Great Hall to uplift the spirits of the Lady.

One day the elder nephew of Sir Thomas arrived at the castle. A manly lad of five and twenty, Uther Tresyllian was heir to the castle and all its contents should his uncle's marriage fail to bear fruit. Uther and his young aunt soon became close companions and could often be seen wandering together along the moor or the seashore.

Now the laughter of the Lady enlivened the corridors of the castle, and everyone was glad of the pleasant change in atmosphere. Everyone, that is, but Thomas Tresyllian, who arrived home from Scotland to find his heir and his bride embracing in the chapel.

Sir Thomas accepted not this indiscretion. He banished Uther forever from the Cornish coast and ordered that his Lady be bricked up alive within the cellar walls. The young bride perished in her agony. Sir Thomas died on the battlefields of Normandy. And the second eldest nephew inherited the estate.

Shortly thereafter, a woeful spirit was seen flitting through the dank corridors of Tresyllian Castle. Her long pale hair was loosed from its braid and a silvery-white gown clothed her slender figure. To this day, the White Lady haunts the ancient tower, seeking a final resting place for her bones and lasting peace for her soul.

# Planetfall

Preface to the Story

After the fall of the Second Galactic Union in 1716 GY, a ten-thousand-year dark age settled upon the galaxy. Interstellar travel was non-existent , and many star systems descended into a near-barbaric state, burning coal and gas for energy, and growing food directly from exposed topsoil. In 11,203 GY, a treaty between the Empires of Tremain and Galium formed the Third Gallictic Union. Ships of the Stellar Patrol (a pseudo-military wing of the Union government on Tremain) began exploring the galaxy, searching for the human civilizations that are the remnants of the Second Union. You are a native of the planet Gallium. Although it is one of the most politically powerful worlds in the Union, Gallium is no garden spot. In fact, the Gallium Chamber of Commerce brochure entitled "Ten Great Reasons to Visit Gallium" ends on page 3. The author ran out of reasons after listing just two. For five generations, your family has served in the Stellar Patrol. Your great-great-grandfather was a High Admiral and one of the founding officers of the Patrol. It was taken for granted that when you came of age you would join up. Now, more than a year after signing up, and two months after being transferred to the S.P.S. Feinstein, you are still only ranked Ensign Seventh Class. Your superior officer, Ensign First Class Blather, has been making your life miserable. You're beginning to wonder if you're really cut out for the Stellar Patrol...

About the Author

Steve Meretzky (1957- ) was born and raised in Yonkers, NY, where his early hobbies included rooting for the New York Mets and against Richard Nixon. A few historians of interactive fiction think that Meretzky's first job, packing nuts and bolts for his father's hardware business, was the formative moment of his writing career. A few other people think that there's absolutely no connection. Most people don't think about it at all. Meretzky arrived at the Massachusetts Institute of Technology in September of 1975 to pursue a career in architecture. MIT's Department of Architecture convinced Meretzky that he should pursue a career in Construction Management. Following his unexpected graduation, several construction firms convinced Meretzky that he should pursue a career as a game tester for Infocom. Finally, by 1982, Marc Blank had convinced Meretzky that he should pursue a career as an author of interactive fiction ("implementor" in Infocom lingo). Along with Infocom's Dave Lebling, Meretzky is the first person admitted to the Science Fiction Writers of America for authoring interactive fiction.

# THE PATROL'S LOOKING FOR A FEW GOOD ORGANISMS

When the Third Galactic Union was formed by the Great Treaty of 11, 203 GY between the Empires of Tremain and Gallium, an order went forth from the capital on Tremain that a great armada be formed.

The greatest military and philanthropic in the Galaxy, including High Admiral Merescu and the Lord Beatitude Berezza, were sequestered in a brightly lit map room for a week-long intensive brainstorming session. No records were kept of this top-secret strategic summit, but out of it came the most ambitious apostolic pseudo-military unit ever conceived. The seven-day conference changed the course of intergalactic exploration and diplomacy forever.

First, blueprints for huge multipurpose starships were drawn up. Next, designers from Vandermeek, the fashion capital of the Universe, were commissioned to create the perfect uniform: functional, comfortable, and virtually indestructible. Finally, a highly sophisticated, incredibly accurate weapon prototype was assembled.

Appeals for soldiers appeared in all Third Union publications, as well as on all subspace frequencies. Almost immediately, the ranks were filled and a waiting list was established.

Thus was the Stellar Patrol born, and our mission ever since has been to explore the Galaxy, to seek out such remnants of human civilization as have managed to survive the Second Union's collapse and the Dark age that followed - in short, to "Boldly Go Where Angels Fear to Tread."

# DO YOU HAVE WHAT IT TAKES?

The Stellar Patrol is like a giant, ever-growing benevolent bird: its top leaders the brain, its commanders the wings, its starships the body, its strong recruits the backbone and muscle, its discoveries the energy that makes it fly, its weak recruits the bodily waste that gets left behind. Carelessness and laziness have no place in the Stellar Patrol: recruits must be strong, brave, and resourceful. Recruits must be able to laugh in the face of death, sneer in the clutches of adversity, and eat almost anything. Loyalty to the Union must be limitless and unconditional, and dedication to a project - be it building a space pod, exploring a new planet, or shining a superior's shoes - must be absolute.

In short, if you are the kind of organism who can stare 10,000 years of darkness straight in the visual receptor without flinching - if you can stand up to the horrors of star systems descended to near-barbarism, where uncivilized beings live savagely in primitive shelters rudely constructed of coarse minerals and deceased vegetation - then you may just have what it takes to be a part of our proud tradition.

Cadet 4th Class Darrell Plintiv is a fine example of the kind of being today's Stellar Patrol produced. Let his story serve as an inspiration to all.

# THE PATROL MADE ME INTO AN ORGANISM MY PROGENITORS CAN BE PROUD OF.

"I'm part of a team devoted to excellence and enterprise that is the Stellar Patrol's proud tradition," says Cadet 4th Class Darrell Plintiv. "In my three years with the Patrol, I've found plenty of opportunity for advancement. And I've seen solar systems never before visited by the Third Union, some inhabited only by crystalline-based life forms! Sure, life in the Patrol isn't always a thrill-a-millichron, but they've developed a wide range of activities to improve my mind and encourage personal growth. You have to be strong, brave, and resourceful. I'm gaining invaluable experience that can lead to a high-paying civilian career in later life. And my uniform is functional, comfortable, and virtually indestructible!"

The Stellar Patrol builds character. You learn new cultures and new ways of thinking. You learn to survive hardships both mental and physical. You learn how to withstand pain - and be proud of it. If you're the type of organism we're looking for, read on.

# LEARN VALUABLE SKILLS AND EXPLORE THE GALAXY.

Sure, you'll get a paycheck in the Patrol. But 32 credits, new underwear, and a pack of chewing gum every month isn't all you'll get out of it. You'll also be traveling to distant worlds you never imagined existed, earning the respect of your friends and family, and acquiring outstanding technical training that can get you a good job in later life. Here are just a few of the valuable skills you can learn in the patrol.

## HOW TO BECOME A FAST LEARNER

As a new recruit to the Stellar Patrol, you will spend your first four weeks in Intelligence Camp. There, you will be taught the most essential knowledge in the Universe using highly advanced intensive studying techniques. You'll learn to read and speak the 18 principal languages of the Galaxy fluently in three days. You'll memorize the structural formula, molecular weight, melting point, boiling point, density, and solubility of every known organic and inorganic compound in two days; thermodynamic properties (including temperature, heat, and entropy of transition) of all elements and oxides in one day; and all 300 astrophysics log tables overnight. Other areas of study will include general nuclear phenomena, isotopes, radioactivity, fusion, antimatter, the origin of life, the classification and metabolisms of organisms, energy, transportation, religion, and philosophy.

It might take an unenlisted civilian months, even years, to learn all this essential knowledge. But the Stellar Patrol is staffed with the Third Union's finest educators and electric shock therapists to guarantee that all recruits learn FAST.

## HOW TO BE STRONG

After Intelligence Camp, you will spend six to 10 weeks in Boot Camp. There, every muscle we can find in your body, from your frontalis to your abductor of hallux, will be stretched, trained, toned, and hardened. Scrawny recruits will become muscular powerhouses; corpulent recruits will become lithe, quick, and sinewy. Only high-protein no-fiber diets will be dished out. To build up endurance, you will be permitted little or no rest time. Recreation activities will stress the importance of physical fitness: moving mounds of dirt from location to location, 20-kilometer jogs, boxing, sprinting, and 30-kilometer jogs. You will sweat your old body away and run it into the ground beyond recognition, and emerge from Boot Camp with a better-than-new physique of Gurtharkian proportions.

What a challenge!

## HOW TO BECOME A LEADER

Since its inception, the Stellar Patrol has always looked for individuals who shine. (We also look for celestial bodies that shine - ask for our full-color brochure entitled "Exploring Cosmic Phenomena.")

To gain recognition and eventually serve the Patrol in leadership capacity, you should volunteer often for the toughest assignments: front line combat, reconnaissance missions, and grotch cage cleaning detail. It takes a very special soldier to recognize the potential that can be realized from the last-mentioned line of duty.

# HOW TO USE YOUR TIME EFFECTIVELY

Because life in the Stellar Patrol can't always be a thrill-a-millichron, we've developed a wide range of activities to improve your mind and encourage personal growth. One of the more popular - and profitable - ways to fill time between orbit watch shifts is to enroll in the Deep Space Hero Correspondence Course, (Since the Patrol places such a high premium on education, we will match - credit for credit - all funds you set aside for schooling. Ask your recruiter for details.)

# WE'LL TELL YOU WHERE TO GO

For more than 140 Galactic years, Stellar Patrol ships have been visiting foreign ports and exploring exotic planets - some inhabited only by crystalline-based life forms. But the excitement doesn't stop there.

You'll explore solar systems never before visited by the Third Union. You'll teach Galalingua to children on Flemring-5. You'll see nebulea and novas. You'll hear the haunting music of the Stringface species on Brylyn Minor. You'll watch the double sunset and triple moonrise from Legllama.

In the Patrol, you'll enjoy shore leave at exotic ports like Accardi-3. At the famed Thieves Bazaar you'll haggle for exotic placebo treasures, and at the Scavengers Market you'll find great buys on grotchbone carvings and ivory receptor shades. The multi-level swimming crater on Accardi-3 is the largest in the Universe. Also on Accardi-3 is the blindingly beautiful Refractory Wall, a 10-megameter natural formation composed of glistening crystal.

But no matter where your stationed or on-duty in the Universe, you'll be welcomed by all life forms, because you're a member of he Third Union's Stellar Patrol, part of a team devoted to the excellence and enterprise that is the Stellar Patrol's proud tradition.

# TAKE COMMAND OF YOUR TOMORROW TODAY

You may start out at the bottom as Ensign 7th, but you won't have to stay that way for long, because there's plenty of opportunity for advancement in the Patrol for those who live up to our motto, " Boldly Going Where Angels Fear to Tread."

To ensure the future of your choice, be sure to tell your recruiter about the kind of job you're interested in when you enlist. (Enlistment is conditional pending on your results of the qualifications test, at the end of this brochure.) Your recruiter will do everything possible to put you in that line of duty. Occasionally a position you're interested in is temporarily filled, or will require experience in another Stellar Patrol position. If so, your recruiter can recommend your surest route to success. The following is but a sampling of the many fine ways you can serve the Patrol while gaining invaluable experience that can lead to high-paying civilian careers in later life.

**Galactoturf Farmer (GF)** - GF's are responsible for the growth and maintenance of all artificial green surfaces. When the Patrol is in orbit, all aboard-ship training is done on this material. Comparable civilian careers: lawn analyst, ground crew supervisor, and rug-maintenance manager.

**Grotch Breeder (GB)** - GB's play an important role in the very survival of the Patrol. Without the grotch, zero-gravity lab experiments would have to be performed on crew members. Qualified applicants must be immune to grotch venom. One year's service as a GB counts as four credits toward an advanced degree in cosmobiology at most accredited learning centers. Comparable civilian careers: zookeeper's assistant and circus sanitation engineer.

**Hull Check Mate (HCM)** - Responsible for the upkeep of all shipboard surfaces. HCM's also instruct crew members in the operation and maintenance of sliding doors. Comparable civilian jobs: gravity enforcement officer and receptor technician.

Morale Officer (MO) - It takes an extraordinarily patient being to serve a Morale Officer. MO's offer guidance and encouragement to hundreds of crew members, and train new recruits to realize that all sickness and injury is in the mind. You must have a kindly countenance and a winning smile (since you alone will establish contact with other ships.) Comparable civilian jobs: riot control officer, suicide counselor, and Double Fanucci referee.

**Mess Service (MS)** - MS's control every aspect of the chow detail - from the ordering of supplies through the serving of well-balanced, appealing meals prepared in artificial-gravity ovens. Excellent equilibrium is necessary. Comparable civilian jobs: scrap metal recycler and faith healer.

**Military Music Maker (MMM)** - MMM's must have talent and a portable instrument to qualify for this exciting duty. Familiarity with at least three chords is essential; two chrons of daily practice will be required. When you learn to play music the Patrol way, fellow beings will stand up and take notice. Also available are positions within the Floating Band. Comparable civilian jobs: teacher for the deaf and Ramosian sheep herder.

**Sleep Technician (ST)** - Because crew members spend so much time in their berths, they must be kept in optimal resting condition. As an ST, you'll oversee complete alignment and cleaning of said sleeping quarters, and monitor the Flexbed automated system designed to prevent inactive muscles from atrophying in space. Two years' experience as a Pillow Fluffer (PF) required. Comparable civilian jobs: social adjustment worker, dry cleaner, and mortician.

**Support Systems Regulator (SSR)** - SSR's have a long and proud history in the Stellar Patrol. Duties include construction, programming, and deprogramming of all shipboard support wywtems. A trorough knowledge of the events leading up to the Great Collapse is necessary. Must be very detail-oriented. Advance degree in computer psychology preferred. Comparable civilian jobs: electronics mastermind and ventriloquist.

**Yosailor (YS)** - Calls troops to meals, to attention, and to combat-ready posture (upright). Although most recruits applying for this position can yodel proficiently,beginners will be auditioned and considered for acceptance. Exceptionally versatile larynx required. Comparable civilian jobs: auctioneer and evangelical preacher.

Regardless of the position you hold in the Stellar Patrol, as a proud member you'll be helping to carry the Third Union's peaceful message of benevolent central bureaucratism to the thousands of worlds lost after the Great Collapse. It takes grit and courage as well as wisdome to be such a messenger. For while most civilized planets can be brought into the fold via a routine ambassadorial mission, certain worlds require further explanation of the importance of 600-page tax returns and forms to be filled out in triplicate. In such cases, its the job of the Patrol to step in, firmly plant its heel, and take charge of that situation. If you have a sharp mind, a quick wit, and the ability to guess between right and wrong, then maybe that heel could be you.

# FIND OUT IF YOU'RE STELLAR PATROL MATERIAL-TODAY!

This incredibly comprehensive questionnaire was prepared totally in accordance with the rules and regulations of the Eighth Division Codes of the Third Galactic Union.

To help your recruitment officer determine the best positions for you when you join the Stellar Patrol, fill out the entire questionnaire honestly and without help from family members or friends.

Note: Although most of this data is on Permafile at Third Galactic Union Central Headquarters and can be verified instantly, this is our only method for determining how closely you adhere to the standard code of honor.

## PHYSICAL ATTRIBUTES

1. Color of eyes: ______________________

   Do you need glasses or corrective surgery on your eyes?

   ☐ yes ☐ no

2. Color of hair: ______________________

   Present hair length: On head: ______________

   Elsewhere (specify): ______________

   Are you bald? ☐ yes ☐ no ☐ receding hairline

3. Height (check one):
   - ☐ Below 1.5 meters but willing to undergo Artificial Elongation Therapy to meet Stellar Patrol requirements
   - ☐ Below 1.5 meters and unwilling to undergo A.E.T.
   - ☐ Between 1.5 and 3 meters
   - ☐ Above 3 meters but willing to undergo Artificial Shrinkage Therapy to meet Stellar Patrol requirements
   - ☐ Above 3 meters and unwilling to undergo A.S.T.

4. Respiratory functions: Can you breathe through your:
   - ☐ nose
   - ☐ mouth
   - ☐ both nose and mouth
   - ☐ neither nose nor mouth
   - ☐ none of the above

   Do you smoke?
   - ☐ often
   - ☐ sometimes
   - ☐ never
   - ☐ never looked

5. How would you describe your overall physical health?
   - ☐ Excellent
   - ☐ Good
   - ☐ Fair
   - ☐ Poor
   - ☐ Notify my next of kin immediately

## EDUCATION/PERSONAL BACKGROUND

6. Have you finished high school or do you know someone who has?
   - ☐ yes
   - ☐ no
   - ☐ not sure

7. I am able to communicate with others:
   - ☐ in Galalingua
   - ☐ in monosyllabic grunts
   - ☐ via Astronmet's Universal Sign Language
   - ☐ not at all

8. Do you have any experience:
   a. using a megaplenoscope? ☐ yes ☐ no
   b. operating a Schistosoma detector? ☐ yes ☐ no
   c. actuating a seroepidemiological cyclodiathermy laser? ☐ yes ☐ no
   d. doing laundry? ☐ yes ☐ no
   e. other (specify): ______________________

9. What are your interests and hobbies? (Check up to three)
   - ☐ Jogging
   - ☐ Traveling
   - ☐ Playing Double Fanucci
   - ☐ Moving mounds of dirt from location to location
   - ☐ Climbing trees
   - ☐ Climbing walls
   - ☐ Writing manuals
   - ☐ Thinking
   - ☐ Thinking out loud/talking to yourself
   - ☐ Filling out questionnaires
   - ☐ Drooling
   - ☐ Scratching
   - ☐ Being miserable
   - ☐ Apologizing
   - ☐ Reading manuals

10. In ten words or less, describe the very reason for your existence:

    ______________________

    ______________________

## PSYCHOLOGICAL PROFILE

11. Which of the following would you be willing to do for your Union?
    - ☐ die
    - ☐ die slowly
    - ☐ die slowly and painfully
    - ☐ read an Infocom instruction manual
    - ☐ none of the above

12. I am most attracted to:
    - ☐ beings who are superior to myself in rank
    - ☐ beings of the opposite sex
    - ☐ beings of the same sex
    - ☐ beings of no sex
    - ☐ myself

13. Do you suffer from any mental disorders that would prevent you from participating in laboratory experiments?
    - ☐ it doesn't matter; I'll do whatever I'm told
    - ☐ no
    - ☐ definitely not

14. My favorite form of recreation is:
    - ☐ mopping up after slimy beings who are superior to myself in rank
    - ☐ dueling with laser bazookas at two paces
    - ☐ forcing people to read Infocom manuals

15. Do you enjoy working with:

| | | |
|---|---|---|
| people? | ☐ yes | ☐ no |
| animals? | ☐ yes | ☐ no |
| plants? | ☐ yes | ☐ no |
| aliens? | ☐ yes | ☐ no |
| finger paints? | ☐ yes | ☐ no |

16. Patience factor: Stand in a corner of the room facing the wall for as long as you can. Don't continue reading until you stop. Now, write here how long you stood: ________ (in days).

17. Hydrophobia factor: Chain yourself to a rock underwater for as long as you can. Don't continue reading until you stop. Now, write here how long you held your breath: ________ (in days).

18. Monotony factor: Repeat number 17 above as many times as you can. Don't continue reading until you stop. Now, write here whether you were really gullible enough to repeat number 17: ________ .

## LOGICAL REASONING ABILITIES

19. FOOT is to SHOE as FINGER is to:
    a. Nose
    b. Eye
    c. Ear
    d. Mouse
    e. Donut
    f. Honesty

20. RAIN is to SNOW as GROTCH is to:
    a. Leopard
    b. Hurricane
    c. Amoeba
    d. Cage
    e. a and b, and maybe c and d
    f. 3.14159

21. HULL is to SPACESHIP as SKIN is to:
    a. Glove
    b. Cat
    c. Thermonuclear fusion
    d. Titanium
    e. Burn
    f. Muffin

22. In what year was the Intergalactic Commerce Act passed?

    ______________________________

23. Who invented the light deceleration process known as slow glass?

    ______________________________

24. Name the act passed in 11,205 GY to strengthen the Planetary Commerce Act. ______________

25. Name the year in which Arnold Guunuf invented slow glass.

    ______________________________

26. The Intergalactic Commerce Act, passed in 11,205 GY, strengthened what earlier act? ______________

27. In 11,210, a glazier named Arnold Guunuf invented a light deceleration process. Name it. ______________

28. What is the answer to this question?

29. Three couples (the Phariixes, the Boorbs, and the Keqrees) were seated at a circular table playing Partnership Fanucci. They were a cosmobiologist, a gravity engineer, a sleep technician, an ambassador, a fusion supervisor, and an editor; and they were originally from Gallium, Legllama, Granjil-6, Storvbay, Ansill, and Jaaggo. Each male sat between two females, and no one sat next to their spouse.
    From the following information, determine where each person sat, what profession each had, and what planet each came from.
    a. The Ansillan sat between the cosmobiologist and one of the Keqrees.
    b. The female Phariix was seated across the table from the gravity engineer.
    c. The male on the fusion supervisor's left sat across from the person from Granjil-6.
    d. The ambassador was seated between the Jaaggoian and the editor. One of these three was the male Boorb.
    e. The Storvbayite sat on the right of the Galliumian. Neither of them was a Keqree.
    f. The sleep technician sat across from the Legllaman. One of them sat next to the fusion supervisor.

30. Four robotic satellites were designed to do the following: YA3 to find drifting garbage, JP7 to transport the garbage, SEM6 to turn the garbage into energy, and MD8 to distribute the energy. As Destiny would have it, however, YA3 found more drifting garbage than the other three satellites could process. Based on the following clues, determine who designed the satellites.
    a. YA3 did not understand signals transmitted in Galalinguan.
    b. JP7 made no distinction between garbage and energy.
    c. SEM6 made no distinction between garbage and YA3.
    d. MD8 transmitted signals to YA3 only in Galalinguan.

Submit this completed questionnaire to a Stellar Patrol recruiter. If you qualify for the Patrol, you will be notified within two chrons.

# STELLAR PATROL OF THE THIRD GALACTIC UNION

11,344 JULY 22 - TRANSFERRED FROM S.P.S. TRILOBYTE TO S.P.S. FEINSTEIN FOR THE THIRD OF MY FOUR TOURS OF DUTY. I'M TRULY GOING TO MISS MY COMMANDER, ENSIGN FIRST CLASS LIM. HE WAS A FRIEND IN EVERY RESPECT — SOMEONE YOU COULD ALWAYS GO TO WITH A PROBLEM, SOMEONE I COULD REALLY LOOK UP TO. WE WOULD SOMETIMES TALK LONG INTO THE NIGHT. HE WOULD TELL ME ABOUT HIS HOME WORLD OF ASH-DOWN FIVE, AND I WOULD TALK ABOUT GROWING UP ON GALLIUM. I'D GET PRETTY HOMESICK SOMETIMES, EVEN THOUGH GALLIUM IS NOT EXACTLY ONE OF THE GARDEN SPOTS OF THE UNIVERSE. I JUST HOPE MY NEW COMMANDER IS HALF AS NICE AS LIM.

THIS NEW SHIP SEEMS PRETTY SWELL. I'M IN A CABIN WITH ONLY FIVE OTHER ENSIGNS, AND I'VE GOT ONE-AND-A-HALF CUBIC METERS OF LOCKER SPACE!

11,344 JULY 23 – MET MY NEW COMMANDER TODAY – ENSIGN CADET FIRST CLASS BLATHER. HE SEEMS LIKE A REAL KRIP. (EXCUSE THE LANGUAGE, DIARY.) BUT THAT MIGHT JUST BE A BAD FIRST IMPRESSION.

11,344 JULY 25 – ONE OF MY CABIN MATES, GORUND, ORGANIZED A DOUBLE FANUCCI TOURNAMENT AMONG ALL THE ENSIGNS SEVENTH CLASS. WE WERE PLAYING DURING THE 150-MILLICHRON REC PERIOD AFTER LUNCH, AND BLATHER BURST IN AND CONFISCATED THE SETS AND TOLD US THAT PLAYING WAR GAMES WAS A VIOLATION OF PATROL REGULATIONS. BUT ENSIGN WHIRP, WHO'S STUDYING TO BE A PATROL LAWYER, SAID SHE COULDN'T FIND ANYTHING ABOUT IT IN THE REGULATIONS ANYWHERE.

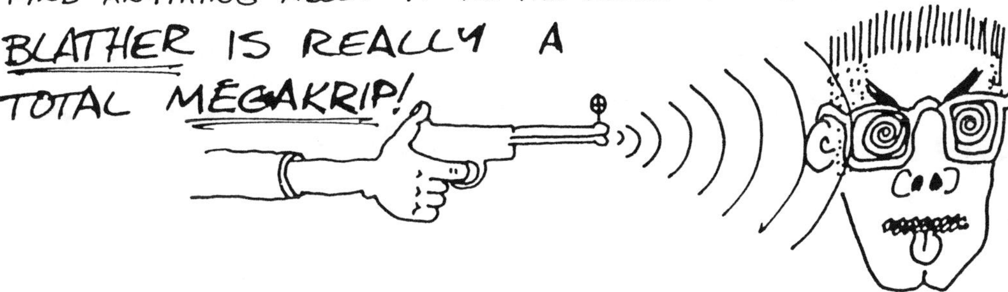

11,344 JULY 28 - I WENT TO SEE THE PERSONNEL OFFICER TODAY TO FIND OUT WHAT MY NEW DUTIES WOULD INVOLVE. HE SHOWED ME A LIST OF ALL THE OPEN ASSIGNMENTS, AND I DECIDED TO PUT IN FOR THE GROTCH-FEEDING DETAIL. WE PICKED UP A FEW GROTCHES WHEN WE WERE ON CRASSUS, AND WE'RE TAKING THEM TO THE ZOOLOGY LABS ON TREMAIN SO THAT MAYBE THEY CAN FIGURE OUT HOW AN ANIMAL CAN PRODUCE 47 TIMES ITS WEIGHT IN TROT EVERY DAY.

11,344 BOZBAR 7 - EVERYONE FROM THE P.O. TO THE SHIP'S COOK HAS APPROVED MY APPLICATION FOR THE GROTCH-FEEDING DETAIL - EXCEPT BLATHER. I HAVE AN APPOINTMENT TO SEE HIM TOMORROW. WISH ME LUCK.

11,344 BOZBAR 8 — **TROT!!** BLATHER REJECTED MY APPLICATION! AND TO MAKE IT WORSE, HE SAID THAT SINCE I SEEM TO LOVE GROTCHES SO MUCH, HE'S ASSIGNING ME TO CLEAN OUT THEIR CAGES. **TROT AND DOUBLE TROT!!**

11,344 BOZBAR 26 - I HAVEN'T HAD TIME TO WRITE IN THIS DIARY LATELY, BECAUSE BLATHER'S BEEN WATCHING US ALL LIKE A TELERAN BIRD. ALSO, LAST WEEK HE FOUND THE DIARY DURING A SURPRISE INSPECTION, GAVE ME 200 DEMERITS, AND TOLD ME THAT DIARIES WERE AGAINST REGULATIONS. BUT I'LL BE FROBBED IF I'M GOING TO STOP. I'VE STARTED HIDING THE DIARY INSIDE MY OFFICIAL DOCUMENTS FILE, AND I KEEP THAT HIDDEN IN THE AIR DUCT. FROM NOW ON I'LL HAVE TO SNEAK AWAY SOMEWHERE WHEN I'M WRITING.

11,344 BOZBAR 27 – GREETINGS FROM THE DECK FOUR SUPPLY CLOSET OF THE S.P.S. FEINSTEIN. I HOPE I'M NOT TEMPTING FATE, SNEAKING AROUND WITH MY DIARY THIS WAY. I USED TO BE AS MUCH OF A DISBELIEVER IN DESTINY AS THE NEXT GUY, BUT NOT ANYMORE. NOT SINCE THE TIME MY MOM WARNED MY DAD NOT TO TEMPT FATE BY WALKING ACROSS THE ASTRAL PLAINS AFTER DARK, WHEN THE COMPUTERIZED ANALYSIS SHOWED A 43% CHANCE OF RESULTING INJURY. MY DAD, STUBBORN AS ALWAYS, JUST LAUGHED AT HER AND WENT RIGHT ON TAKING HIS NIGHTLY STROLLS. **THE VERY NEXT SUMMER HE WENT WALKING AT NIGHT ON THE PLAINS AND STUMBLED OVER A CRATER AND BRUISED HIS KNEE.** GOSH!

11,344 BOZBAR 28 - WE ENTERED PLANETARY ORBIT TODAY, A NON-HUMAN WORLD CALLED ACCARDI-3 (ALTHOUGH THE NATIVES CALL IT SOMETHING LIKE BLOW'K-BIBBEN-GORDO). THEY'RE NOT OFFICIALLY PART OF THE UNION. THE RUMORS SAY THAT WE'RE PICKING UP A SPECIAL AMBASSADOR TO TAKE BACK TO TREMAIN FOR NEGOTIATIONS ON JOINING THE UNION. TOMORROW WE HAVE TO PUT ON OUR DRESS UNIFORMS FOR SOME SPECIAL WELCOMING CEREMONY.

11,344 AUGUST 2 - I CAUGHT A GLIMPSE OF THE ALIEN AMBASSADOR DURING THE WELCOMING CEREMONIES YESTERDAY. HE LOOKS LIKE A CROSS BETWEEN A TREE TRUNK AND A MELTING ICE CREAM CONE. BUT ANYWAY, THE CEREMONY GOT ME OUT OF CLEANING THE GROTCH CAGES TODAY.

11,344 AUGUST 7 - WENT TO THE MANDATORY PATROL INFORMATIONAL TRI-VISION TRIPLE FEATURE LAST NIGHT. WE SAW "TREATMENT FOR SPACE LICE INFESTATION," "SHORELEAVE SHIRLEY: HOW TO GUARD AGAINST CONTRACTING ALIEN DISEASES," AND "THE OXYGEN TANK: YOUR GALVANIZED BUDDY IN THE VACUUM." BLATHER CONFINED HALF THE ENSIGNS TO QUARTERS FOR HOOTING DURING THE SECOND FEATURE. (THE OTHER HALF HAD FALLEN ASLEEP DURING THE FIRST FEATURE.)

11,344 AUGUST 24 - <u>TROT THAT TROTTING KRIP!</u> I APPLIED FOR ASTROPHYSICS TRAINING FOR THE NEXT QUARTER, BUT BLATHER SAYS MY WORK FOR THE SPECIAL ASSIGNMENT TASK FORCE HASN'T BEEN GOOD

ENOUGH, SO NOT ONLY DID HE REJECT MY ASTROPHYSICS APPLICATION, BUT HE SAYS I'LL HAVE TO TAKE REMEDIAL SCRUBBING NEXT QUARTER. WHAT A TROTTING KRIP!

YOU KNOW, FOR THE FIRST TIME I'M BEGINNING TO HAVE DOUBTS ABOUT WHETHER I'M REALLY CUT OUT FOR THE PATROL. WHEN I WAS GROWING UP ON GALLIUM, IT WAS ALWAYS TAKEN FOR GRANTED THAT I WOULD JOIN UP WHEN I CAME OF AGE. MY FAMILY HAS SERVED IN THE PATROL FOR FIVE GENERATIONS. IN FACT, MY GREAT-GREAT-GRANDFATHER WAS A HIGH ADMIRAL AND ONE OF THE FOUNDING FATHERS OF THE PATROL! BUT I SEEM TO BE PERMANENTLY STUCK AT ENSIGN 7TH, AND BLATHER IS MAKING MY LIFE MISERABLE...

11,344 SEPTEM 4 - WE LEFT HYPERSPACE TODAY AT ABOUT 7600; WEREN'T SCHEDULED TO FOR ABOUT ANOTHER

TWO WEEKS. THE GRAPEVINE SAYS WE HAVE SPECIAL ORDERS TO INVESTIGATE A PLANETARY SYSTEM HERE. APPARENTLY, SOME OF THE ARCHAEOLOGISTS BACK ON VARSHON THINK IT MIGHT HAVE BEEN PART OF THE SECOND UNION. I CAN'T IMAGINE WHY ANYONE WOULD SETTLE OUT HERE IN THIS REMOTE CORNER OF THE GALAXY.

11,344 SEPTEM 5 – THAT KRIP HAS DONE IT AGAIN! I MISSED TWO LITTLE PELLETS OF TROT WHEN I WAS CLEANING OUT THE GROTCH CAGES YESTERDAY, AND BLATHER GAVE ME 100 DEMERITS AND ASSIGNED ME TWO EXTRA SHIFTS OF DECK SCRUBBING – INCLUDING DECK NINE, THE FILTHIEST DECK ON THE SHIP! I'M CONSIDERING ASKING FOR A TRANSFER – OR IF THINGS GET WORSE, I MIGHT EVEN ABANDON SHIP!

# Stationfall

Preface to the Story

After the fall of the Second Galactic Union in 1716 GY, a ten thousand year dark age settled upon the galaxy. Interstellar travel was non-existent. Many star systems descended into a near-barbaric state, burning fossil fuels for energy and growing food directly from exposed topsoil. In 11,203 GY, a treaty between the growing empires of Tremain and Gallium formed the Third Galactic Union, with Tremain as its seat of government. A pseudo-military organization, called the Stellar Patrol, was formed to explore the galaxy, searching for the human civilizations that are the remnants of the Second Union. You are a native of Gallium, one of the most politically powerful but culturally barren worlds of the Union. Your great-great-grandfather was a founding officer of the Stellar Patrol, and for five generations, your family has served in the Patrol. It was always taken for granted that you would sign up as soon as you came of age. Once in the Patrol, you discovered that the exciting career promised in all the Patrol recruitment brochures was nonsense. Your life was drudgery and demerits. The one time you got to see an exotic planet was right after a big parade, when they needed a detail to sweep up all the confetti. Then came your big moment: shipwrecked on a seemingly deserted world, you met an exuberant robotic companion named Floyd. Together, the two of you discovered the secret of that mysterious planet, Resida, and saved it from near destruction. As a result of your heroics, you were offered, and quickly accepted, a juicy promotion. Good-bye Ensign Seventh Class — hello Lieutenant First Class! No more scrubwork! No more bathroom details! No more cleaning grotch cages! Finally, your life in the Stellar Patrol would be as exciting as those brochures had promised! Oh, how naive you'd been. Your daily routine simply replaced tedious scrubwork with tedious paperwork. Since your planetfall on Resida, five long years have dragged by, without a single event worthy of note. Why, just look at today's "thrilling" assignment: scooting over to Space Station Gamma Delta Gamma 777-G 59/59 Sector Alpha-Mu-79 to pick up a supply of Request for Stellar Patrol Issue Regulation Black Form Binders Request Form Forms...

About the Author .

Steve Meretzky (1957- ) was born and raised in Yonkers, NY, where his early hobbies included rooting for the New York Mets and against Richard Nixon. A few historians of interactive fiction think that Meretzky's first job, packing nuts and bolts for his father's hardware business, was the formative moment of his writing career. A few other people think that there's absolutely no connection. Most people don't think about it at all. Stationfall is Meretzky's sixth work of interactive fiction. Along with Infocom's Dave Lebling, Meretzky is the first person admitted to the Science Fiction Writers of America for authoring interactive fiction.

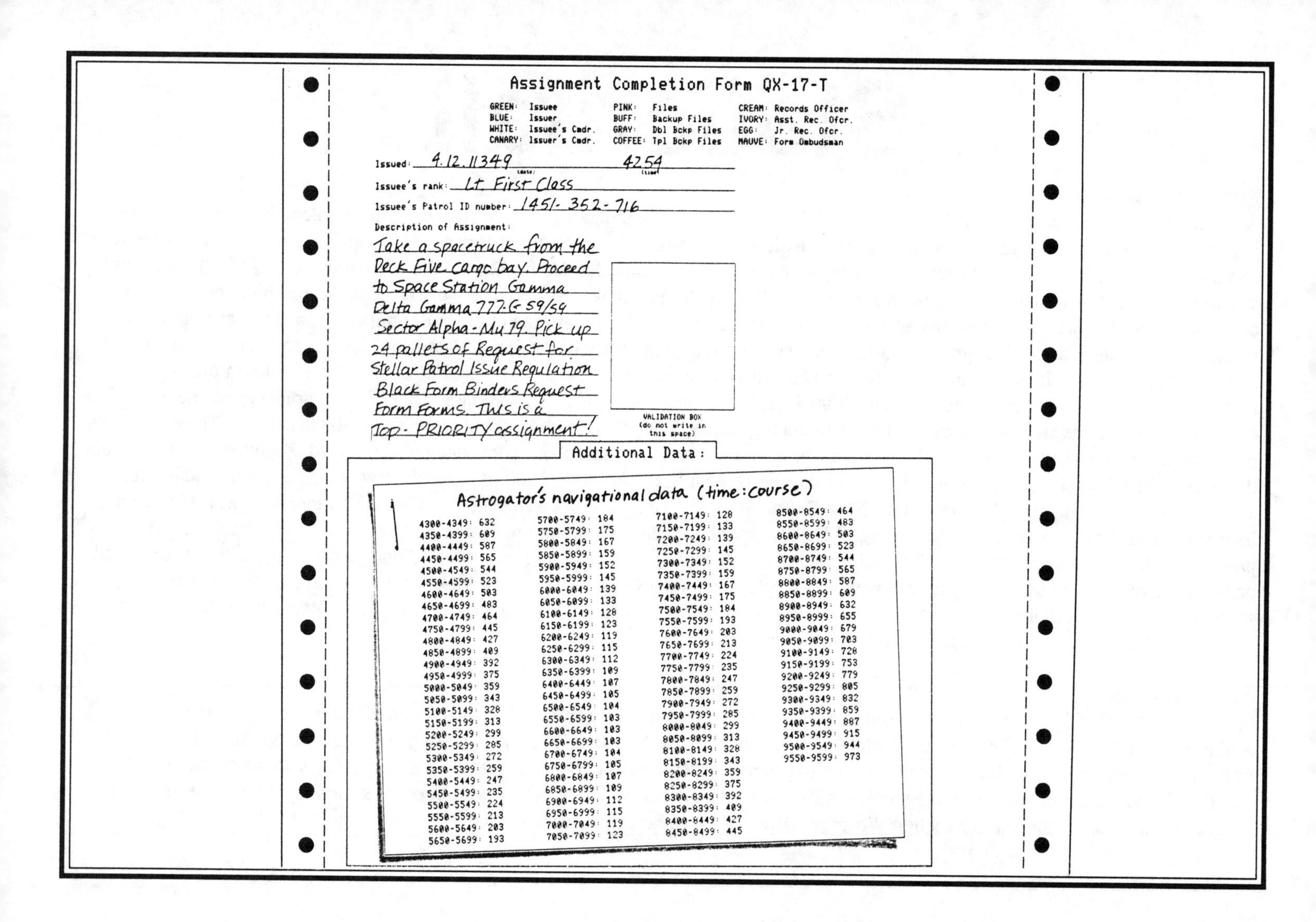

Assignment Completion Form QX-17-T

GREEN: Issuee
BLUE: Issuer
WHITE: Issuee's Cmdr.
CANARY: Issuer's Cmdr.
PINK: Files
BUFF: Backup Files
GRAY: Dbl Bckp Files
COFFEE: Tpl Bckp Files
CREAM: Records Officer
IVORY: Asst. Rec. Ofcr.
EGG: Jr. Rec. Ofcr.
MAUVE: Form Ombudsman

Issued: 4.12.11349 (date) 4254 (time)

Issuee's rank: Lt. First Class

Issuee's Patrol ID number: 1451-352-716

Description of Assignment:

Take a spacetruck from the Deck Five cargo bay. Proceed to Space Station Gamma Delta Gamma 777-G 59/59 Sector Alpha-Mu 79. Pick up 24 pallets of Request for Stellar Patrol Issue Regulation Black Form Binders Request Form Forms. This is a Top-PRIORITY assignment!

VALIDATION BOX
(do not write in this space)

Additional Data:

Astrogator's navigational data (time: course)

| Time | Course | Time | Course | Time | Course | Time | Course |
|---|---|---|---|---|---|---|---|
| 4300-4349 | 632 | 5700-5749 | 184 | 7100-7149 | 128 | 8500-8549 | 464 |
| 4350-4399 | 609 | 5750-5799 | 175 | 7150-7199 | 133 | 8550-8599 | 483 |
| 4400-4449 | 587 | 5800-5849 | 167 | 7200-7249 | 139 | 8600-8649 | 503 |
| 4450-4499 | 565 | 5850-5899 | 159 | 7250-7299 | 145 | 8650-8699 | 523 |
| 4500-4549 | 544 | 5900-5949 | 152 | 7300-7349 | 152 | 8700-8749 | 544 |
| 4550-4599 | 523 | 5950-5999 | 145 | 7350-7399 | 159 | 8750-8799 | 565 |
| 4600-4649 | 503 | 6000-6049 | 139 | 7400-7449 | 167 | 8800-8849 | 587 |
| 4650-4699 | 483 | 6050-6099 | 133 | 7450-7499 | 175 | 8850-8899 | 609 |
| 4700-4749 | 464 | 6100-6149 | 128 | 7500-7549 | 184 | 8900-8949 | 632 |
| 4750-4799 | 445 | 6150-6199 | 123 | 7550-7599 | 193 | 8950-8999 | 655 |
| 4800-4849 | 427 | 6200-6249 | 119 | 7600-7649 | 203 | 9000-9049 | 679 |
| 4850-4899 | 409 | 6250-6299 | 115 | 7650-7699 | 213 | 9050-9099 | 703 |
| 4900-4949 | 392 | 6300-6349 | 112 | 7700-7749 | 224 | 9100-9149 | 728 |
| 4950-4999 | 375 | 6350-6399 | 109 | 7750-7799 | 235 | 9150-9199 | 753 |
| 5000-5049 | 359 | 6400-6449 | 107 | 7800-7849 | 247 | 9200-9249 | 779 |
| 5050-5099 | 343 | 6450-6499 | 105 | 7850-7899 | 259 | 9250-9299 | 805 |
| 5100-5149 | 328 | 6500-6549 | 104 | 7900-7949 | 272 | 9300-9349 | 832 |
| 5150-5199 | 313 | 6550-6599 | 103 | 7950-7999 | 285 | 9350-9399 | 859 |
| 5200-5249 | 299 | 6600-6649 | 103 | 8000-8049 | 299 | 9400-9449 | 887 |
| 5250-5299 | 285 | 6650-6699 | 103 | 8050-8099 | 313 | 9450-9499 | 915 |
| 5300-5349 | 272 | 6700-6749 | 104 | 8100-8149 | 328 | 9500-9549 | 944 |
| 5350-5399 | 259 | 6750-6799 | 105 | 8150-8199 | 343 | 9550-9599 | 973 |
| 5400-5449 | 247 | 6800-6849 | 107 | 8200-8249 | 359 | | |
| 5450-5499 | 235 | 6850-6899 | 109 | 8250-8299 | 375 | | |
| 5500-5549 | 224 | 6900-6949 | 112 | 8300-8349 | 392 | | |
| 5550-5599 | 213 | 6950-6999 | 115 | 8350-8399 | 409 | | |
| 5600-5649 | 203 | 7000-7049 | 119 | 8400-8449 | 427 | | |
| 5650-5699 | 193 | 7050-7099 | 123 | 8450-8499 | 445 | | |

## Robot Use Authorization Form JZ-59-G

| | | | | | |
|---|---|---|---|---|---|
| GREEN: | Issuee | PINK: | Files | CREAM: | Records Officer |
| BLUE: | Issuer | BUFF: | Backup Files | IVORY: | Asst. Rec. Ofcr. |
| WHITE: | Issuee's Cmdr. | GRAY: | Dbl Bckp Files | EGG: | Jr. Rec. Ofcr. |
| CANARY: | Issuer's Cmdr. | COFFEE: | Tpl Bckp Files | MAUVE: | Form Ombudsman |

Issued: 4.12.11349 (date) 4257 (time)

Issuee's rank: Lt. First Class

Issuee's Patrol ID number: 1451-352-716

Applicable robot pool: Deck Five

Instructions to issuee: This form should be presented at the robot pool indicated above. If no such pool exists, return this form to its issuer along with eight completed copies of Missing or Non-Existent Robot Pool Report Form GY-98-M. At the indicated robot pool, this form should be given to any party or parties thereabouts responsible for the discharge of robots, or, if the indicated pool is automated, to the appropriate automated system or systems.

Instructions to robot pool: One robot may be discharged into the care of the issuee of this form for such purposes as are specified under the Stellar Patrol Omnibus Robot Use Policies and Procedures Book. Copies of this form should be sent to the issuee's immediate superior, the ship's Records Officers, Archives One, Two, and Three, the issuee's permanent record file, and the files of the indicated robot pool.

Instructions to robot:

## Class Three Spacecraft Activation Form HB-56-V

| | | | | | |
|---|---|---|---|---|---|
| GREEN: | Issuee | PINK: | Files | CREAM: | Records Officer |
| BLUE: | Issuer | BUFF: | Backup Files | IVORY: | Asst. Rec. Ofcr. |
| WHITE: | Issuee's Cmdr. | GRAY: | Dbl Bckp Files | EGG: | Jr. Rec. Ofcr. |
| CANARY: | Issuer's Cmdr. | COFFEE: | Tpl Bckp Files | MAUVE: | Form Ombudsman |

Issued: 4.12.11349 (date) 4259 (time)

Issuee's rank: Lt. First Class

Issuee's Patrol ID number: 1451-352-716

This form is applicable to the following Class Three vehicles:

TRANS-SPACEDOCK TUGBOAT

FORMS TRANSPORT SPACETRUCK, SIX-METER

FORMS TRANSPORT SPACETRUCK, NINE-METER

FORMS TRANSPORT SPACETRUCK, TWELVE-METER

TITANIUM-HULL SWAMP WALKER

DEEP-SPACE TRANS-ION PARTICLE PLUCKER

AMBASSADORIAL SHUTTLE, ONE-PERSON

AMBASSADORIAL SHUTTLE, TWO-PERSON

AMBASSADORIAL SHUTTLE, MORE-THAN-TWO-PERSON-OR-ONE-PERSON-PLUS-ANY-NUMBER-OF-NON-HUMANS

SCOOTER, INTRA-SYSTEM, CAPTAIN ZOWIE MODEL

ZERO-ENERGY PUDDLE-SITTER, SITTING DUCK BRAND

SEMI-OOFING GIGBUNG-POWERED DOUBLE-FOOZ

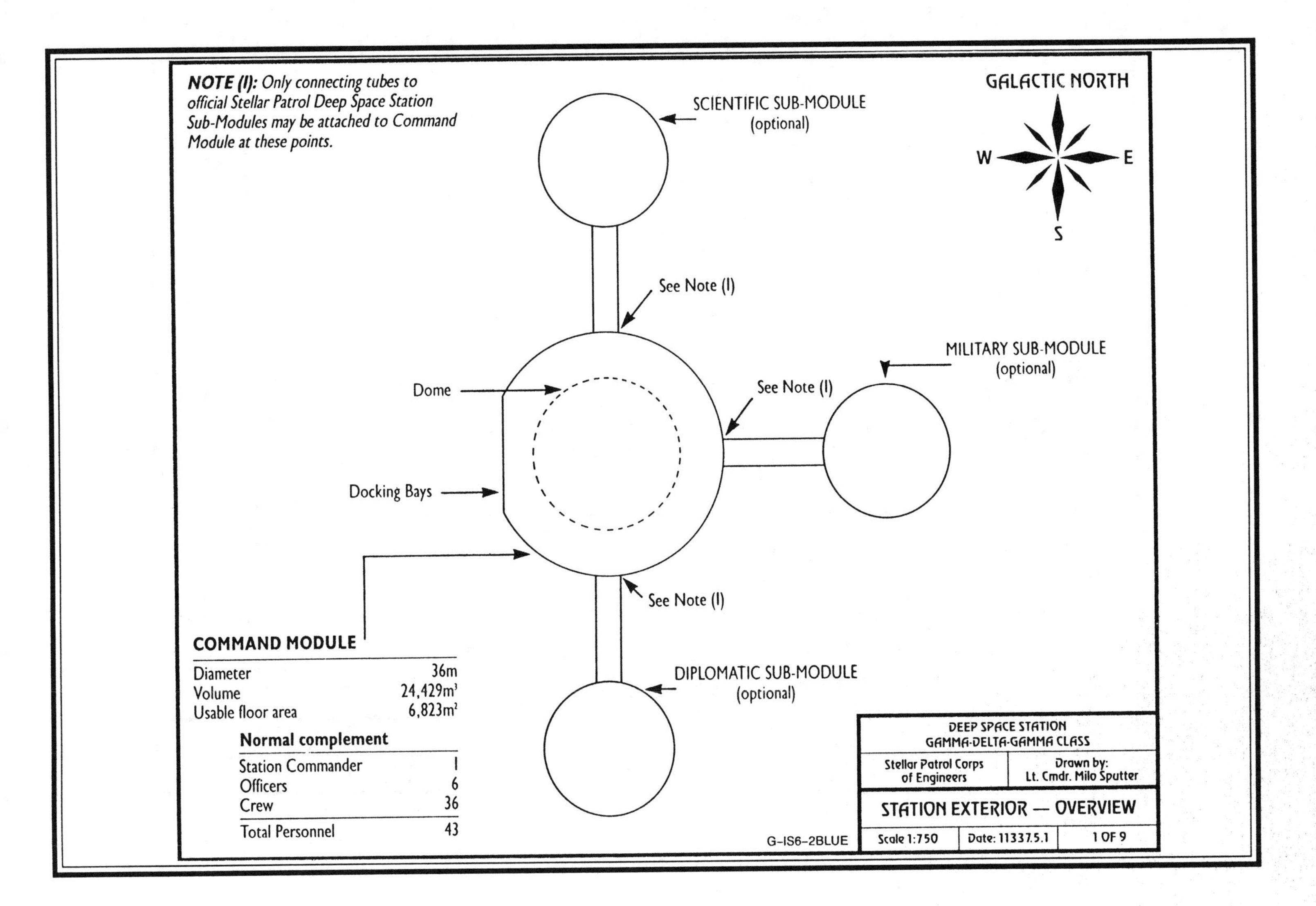

**NOTE (I):** *Only connecting tubes to official Stellar Patrol Deep Space Station Sub-Modules may be attached to Command Module at these points.*
GALACTIC NORTH
W
E
S
SCIENTIFIC SUB-MODULE
(optional)
See Note (I)
MILITARY SUB-MODULE
(optional)
Dome
See Note (I)
Docking Bays
See Note (I)
DIPLOMATIC SUB-MODULE
(optional)
COMMAND MODULE
Diameter 36m
Volume 24,429m³
Usable floor area 6,823m²
Normal complement
Station Commander 1
Officers 6
Crew 36
Total Personnel 43
G–IS6–2BLUE
DEEP SPACE STATION
GAMMA-DELTA-GAMMA CLASS
Stellar Patrol Corps of Engineers
Drawn by: Lt. Cmdr. Milo Sputter
STATION EXTERIOR — OVERVIEW
Scale 1:750
Date: 11337.5.1
1 OF 9

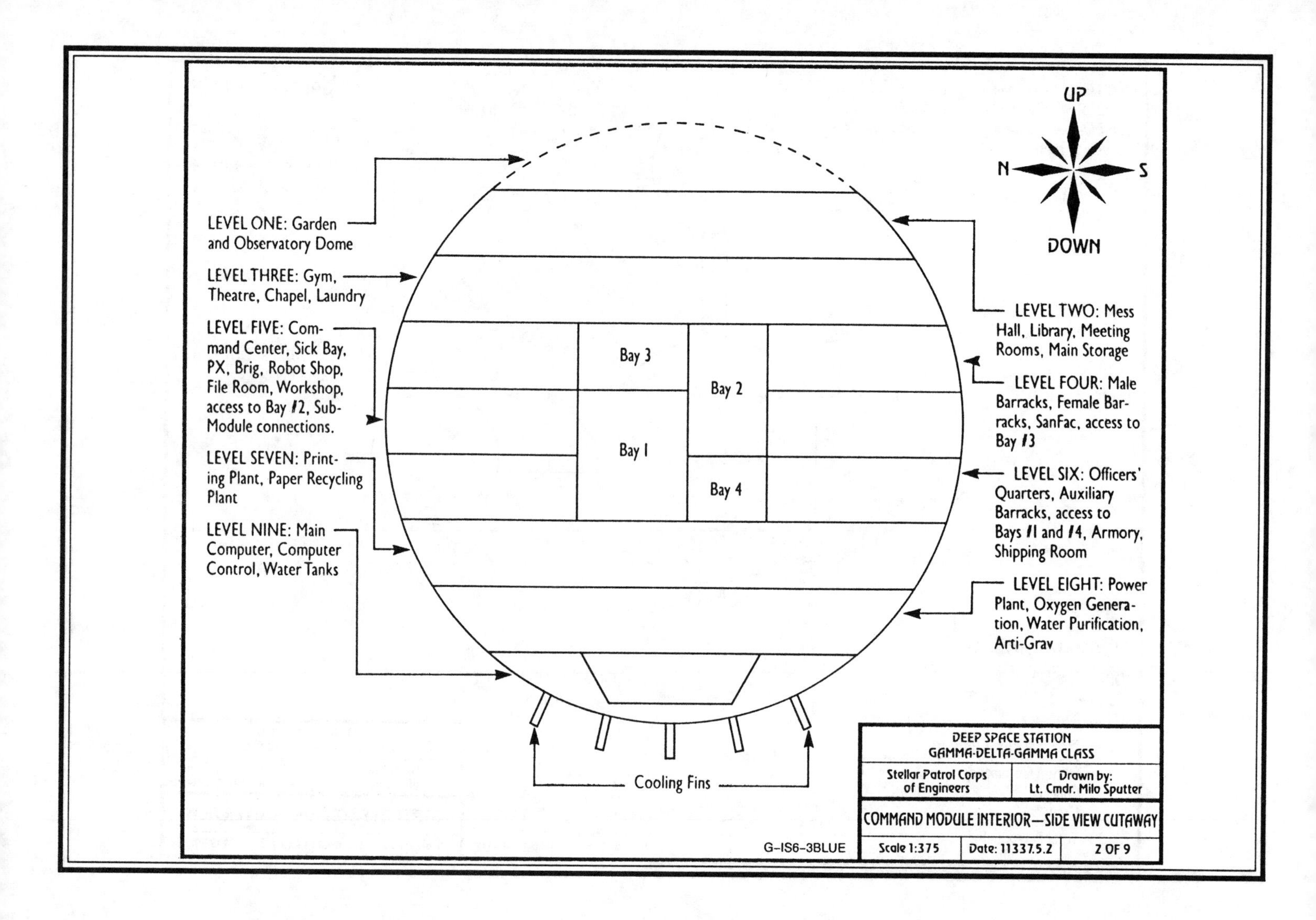
UP
N
S
DOWN
LEVEL ONE: Garden and Observatory Dome
LEVEL THREE: Gym, Theatre, Chapel, Laundry
LEVEL FIVE: Command Center, Sick Bay, PX, Brig, Robot Shop, File Room, Workshop, access to Bay #2, Sub-Module connections.
LEVEL SEVEN: Printing Plant, Paper Recycling Plant
LEVEL NINE: Main Computer, Computer Control, Water Tanks
LEVEL TWO: Mess Hall, Library, Meeting Rooms, Main Storage
LEVEL FOUR: Male Barracks, Female Barracks, SanFac, access to Bay #3
LEVEL SIX: Officers' Quarters, Auxiliary Barracks, access to Bays #1 and #4, Armory, Shipping Room
LEVEL EIGHT: Power Plant, Oxygen Generation, Water Purification, Arti-Grav
Bay 3
Bay 2
Bay 1
Bay 4
Cooling Fins
DEEP SPACE STATION
GAMMA-DELTA-GAMMA CLASS
Stellar Patrol Corps of Engineers
Drawn by: Lt. Cmdr. Milo Sputter
COMMAND MODULE INTERIOR—SIDE VIEW CUTAWAY
Scale 1:375
Date: 11337.5.2
2 OF 9
G-IS6-3BLUE

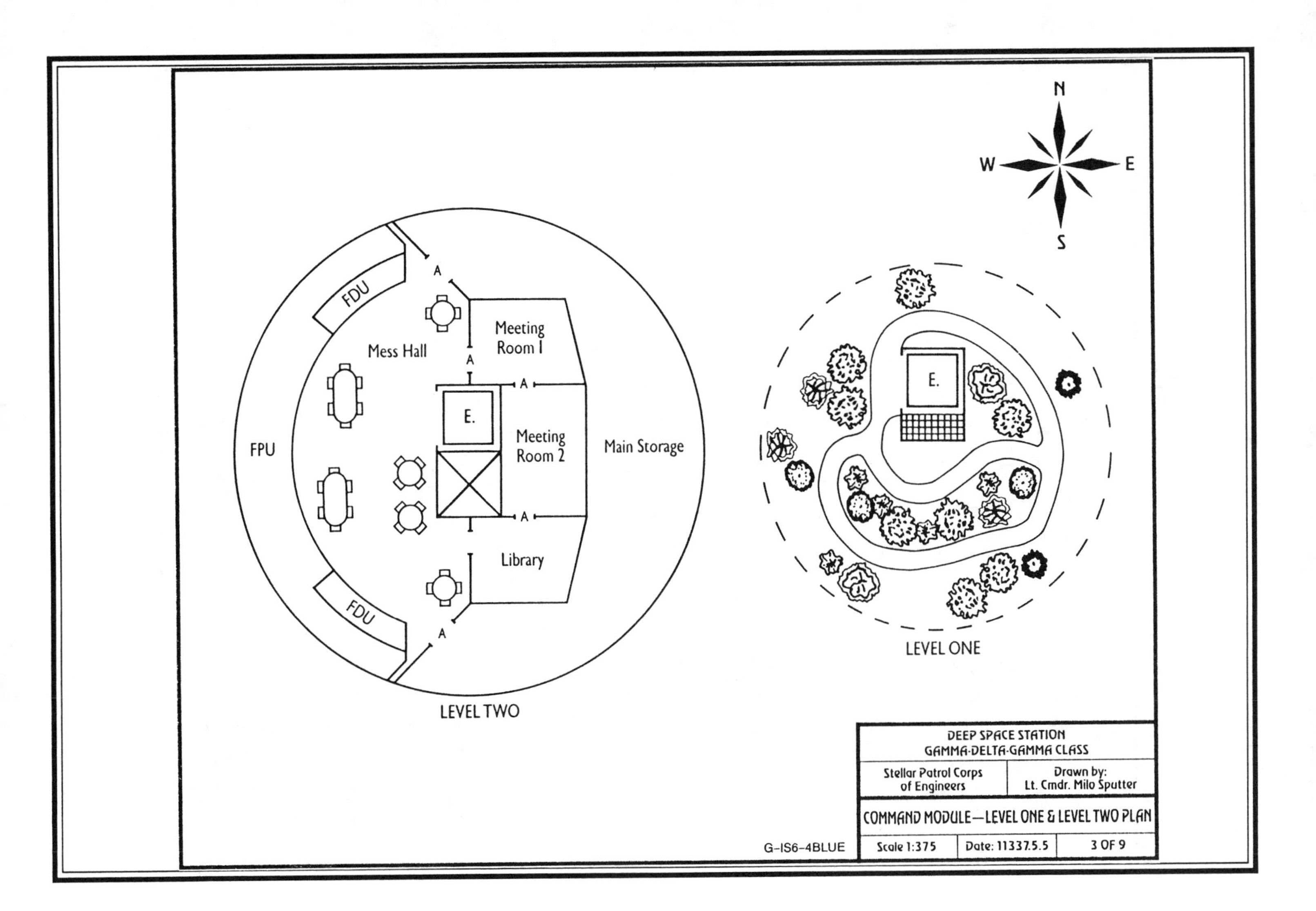
N
W
E
S
FDU
A
Meeting
Room 1
Mess Hall
A
A
E.
Meeting
Room 2
Main Storage
FPU
A
Library
FDU
A
LEVEL TWO
E.
LEVEL ONE
DEEP SPACE STATION
GAMMA-DELTA-GAMMA CLASS
Stellar Patrol Corps
of Engineers
Drawn by:
Lt. Cmdr. Milo Sputter
COMMAND MODULE—LEVEL ONE & LEVEL TWO PLAN
G-IS6-4BLUE
Scale 1:375
Date: 11337.5.5
3 OF 9

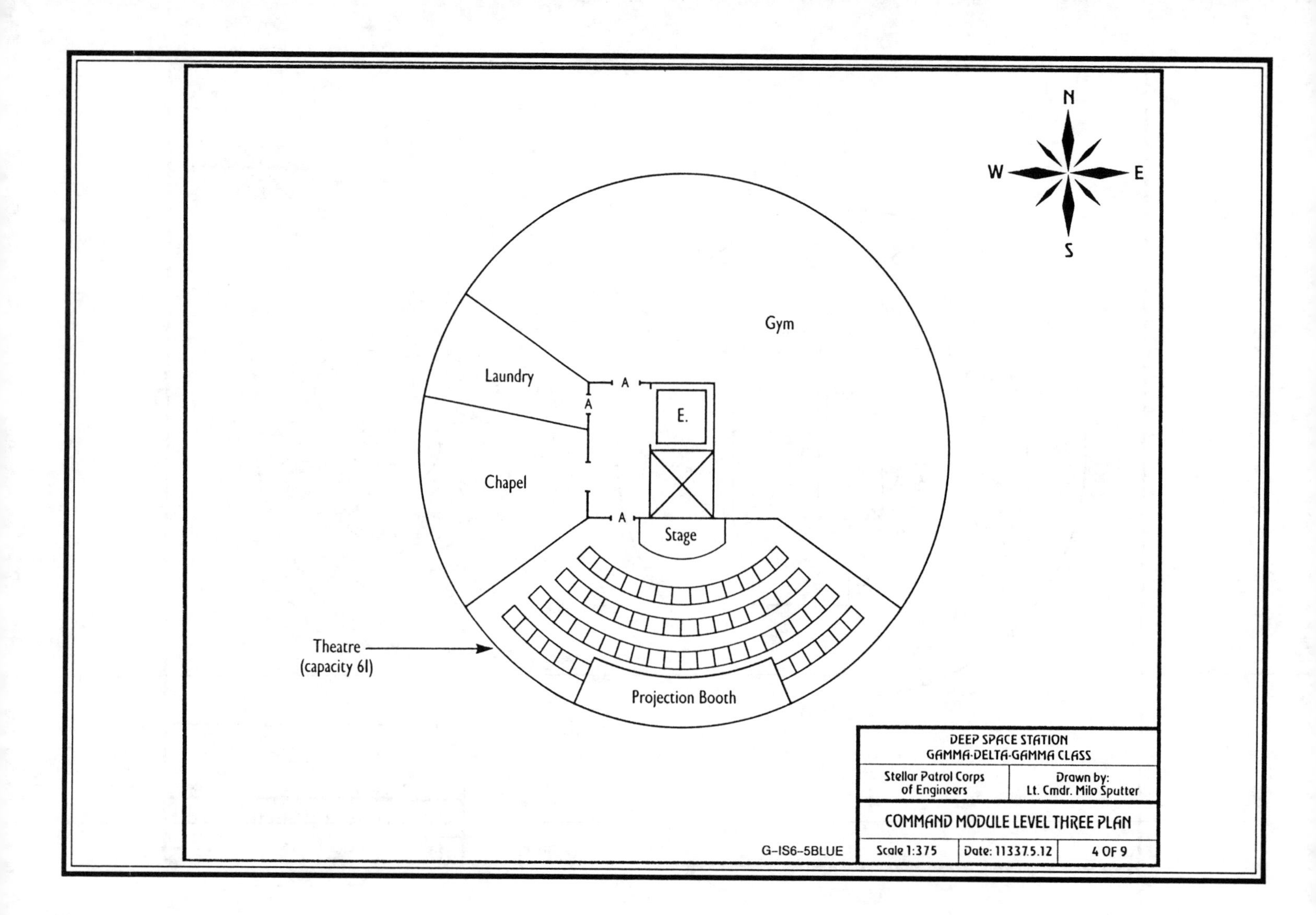
N
W
E
S
Gym
Laundry
A
A
E.
Chapel
A
Stage
Theatre
(capacity 61)
Projection Booth
DEEP SPACE STATION
GAMMA-DELTA-GAMMA CLASS
Stellar Patrol Corps
of Engineers
Drawn by:
Lt. Cmdr. Milo Sputter
COMMAND MODULE LEVEL THREE PLAN
G–IS6–5BLUE
Scale 1:375
Date: 11337.5.12
4 OF 9

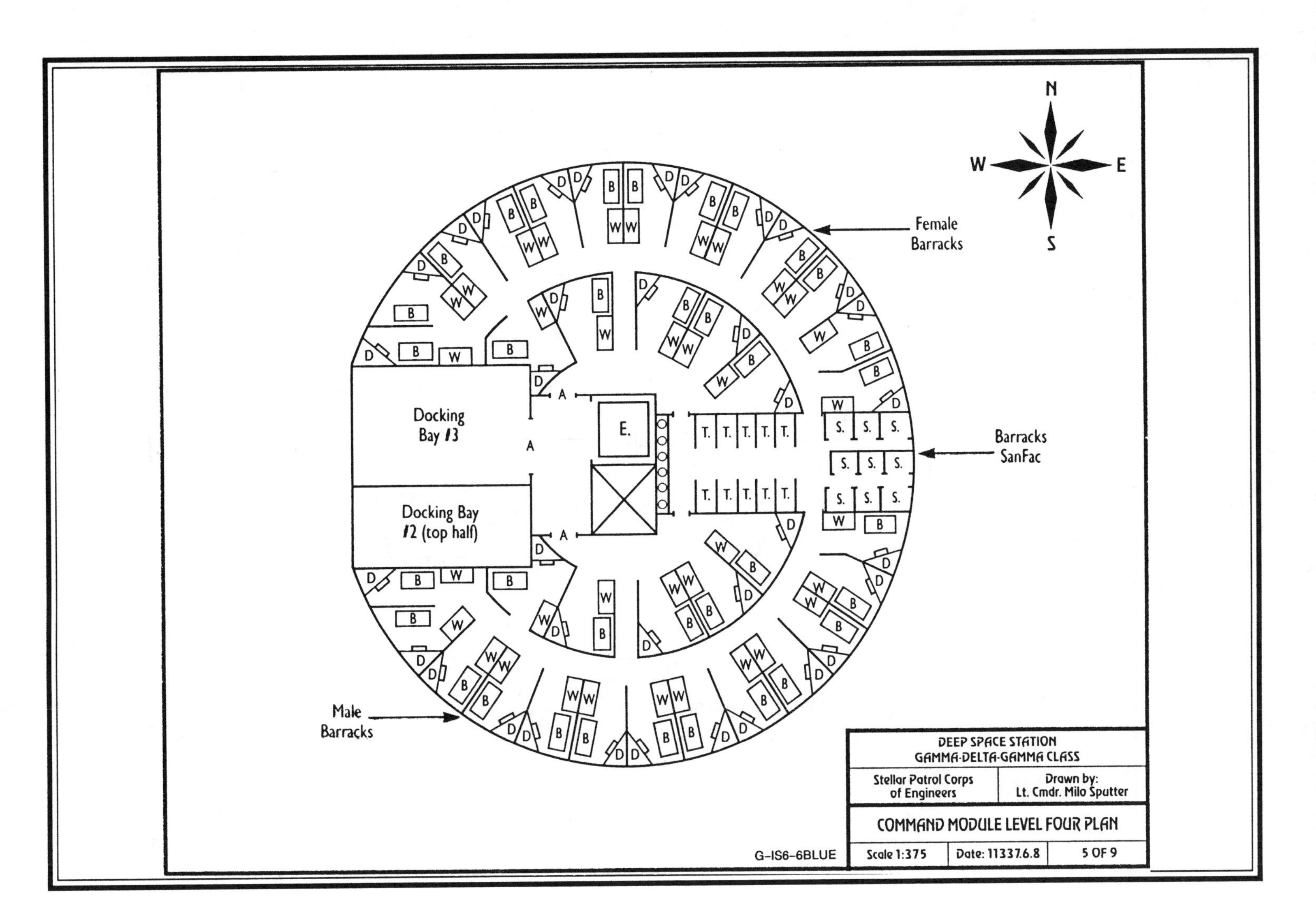
N
W
E
S
Female Barracks
Barracks SanFac
Male Barracks
Docking Bay #3
Docking Bay #2 (top half)
E.
DEEP SPACE STATION
GAMMA-DELTA-GAMMA CLASS
Stellar Patrol Corps of Engineers
Drawn by: Lt. Cmdr. Milo Sputter
COMMAND MODULE LEVEL FOUR PLAN
Scale 1:375
Date: 11337.6.8
5 OF 9
G-IS6-6BLUE

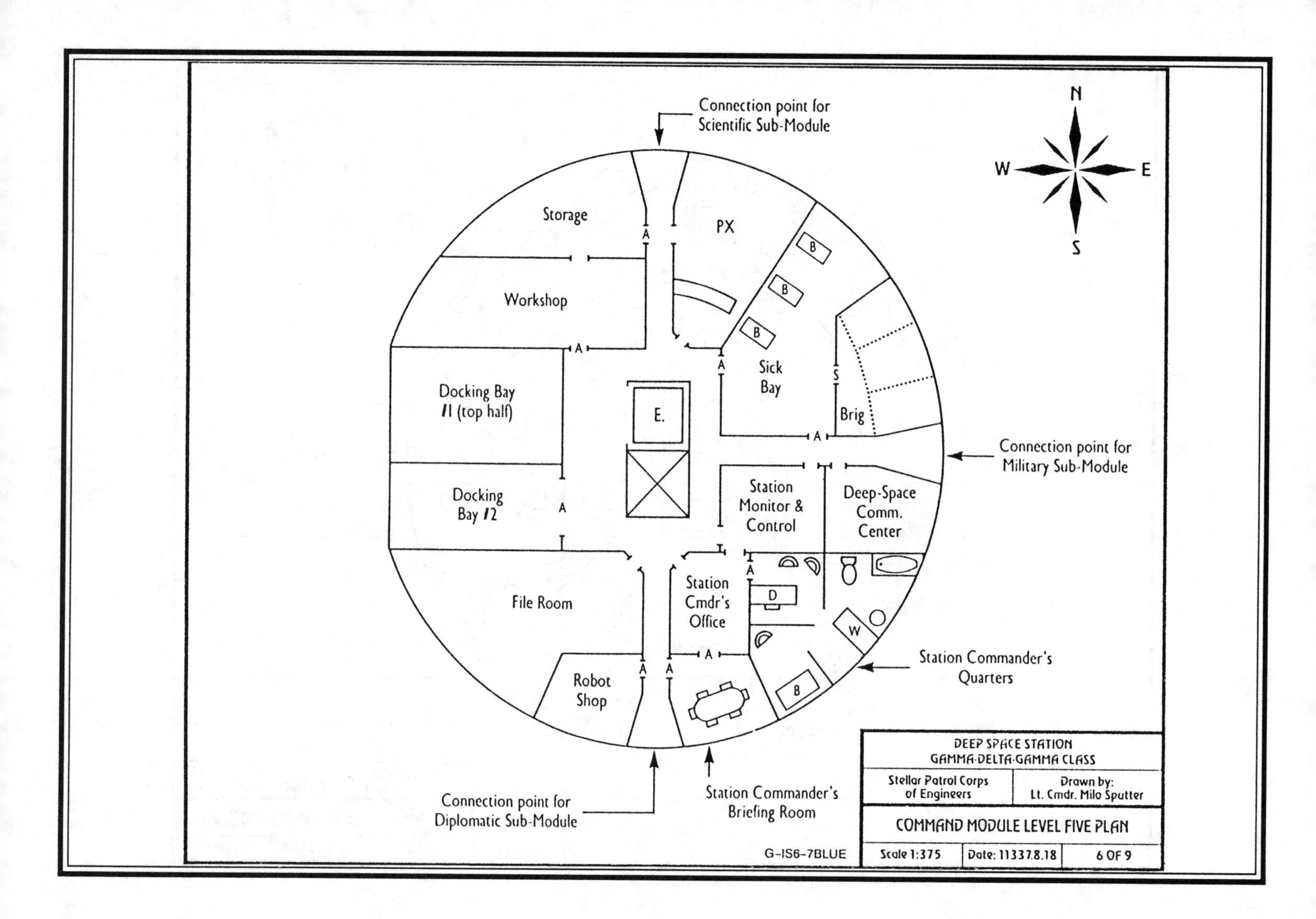
Connection point for
Scientific Sub-Module
N
W
E
S
Storage
PX
A
B
B
B
Workshop
A
A
Sick
Bay
S
Docking Bay
#1 (top half)
E.
Brig
A
Connection point for
Military Sub-Module
Docking
Bay #2
A
Station
Monitor &
Control
Deep-Space
Comm.
Center
A
Station
Cmdr's
Office
D
File Room
W
A
Robot
Shop
A
A
Station Commander's
Quarters
B
DEEP SPACE STATION
GAMMA-DELTA-GAMMA CLASS
Stellar Patrol Corps
of Engineers
Drawn by:
Lt. Cmdr. Milo Sputter
Connection point for
Diplomatic Sub-Module
Station Commander's
Briefing Room
COMMAND MODULE LEVEL FIVE PLAN
G-IS6-7BLUE
Scale 1:375
Date: 11337.8.18
6 OF 9

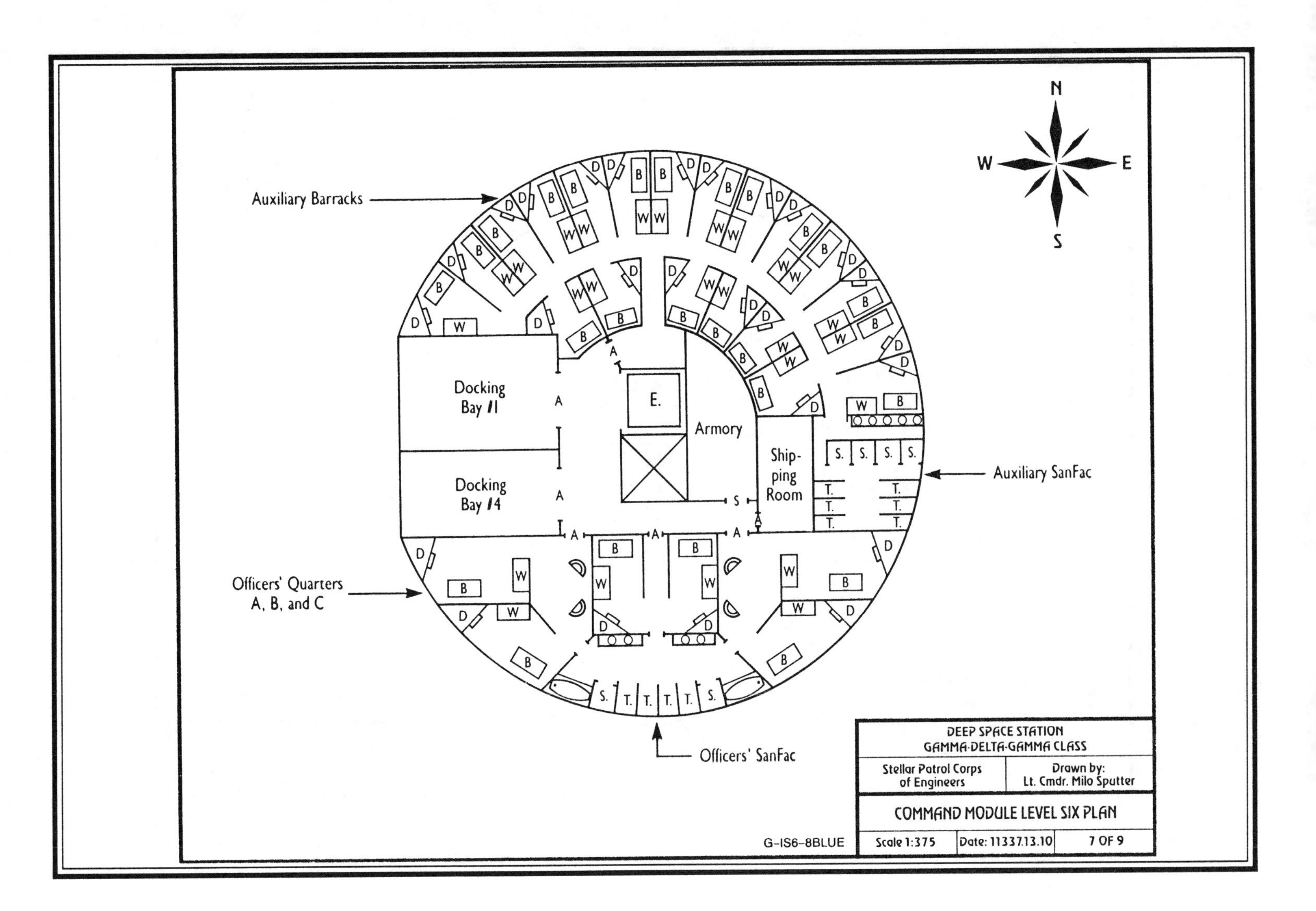
N
W
E
S
Auxiliary Barracks
Docking Bay #1
Docking Bay #4
E.
Armory
Ship-ping Room
Auxiliary SanFac
Officers' Quarters A, B, and C
Officers' SanFac
DEEP SPACE STATION
GAMMA-DELTA-GAMMA CLASS
Stellar Patrol Corps of Engineers
Drawn by: Lt. Cmdr. Milo Sputter
COMMAND MODULE LEVEL SIX PLAN
G-IS6-8BLUE
Scale 1:375
Date: 11337.13.10
7 OF 9

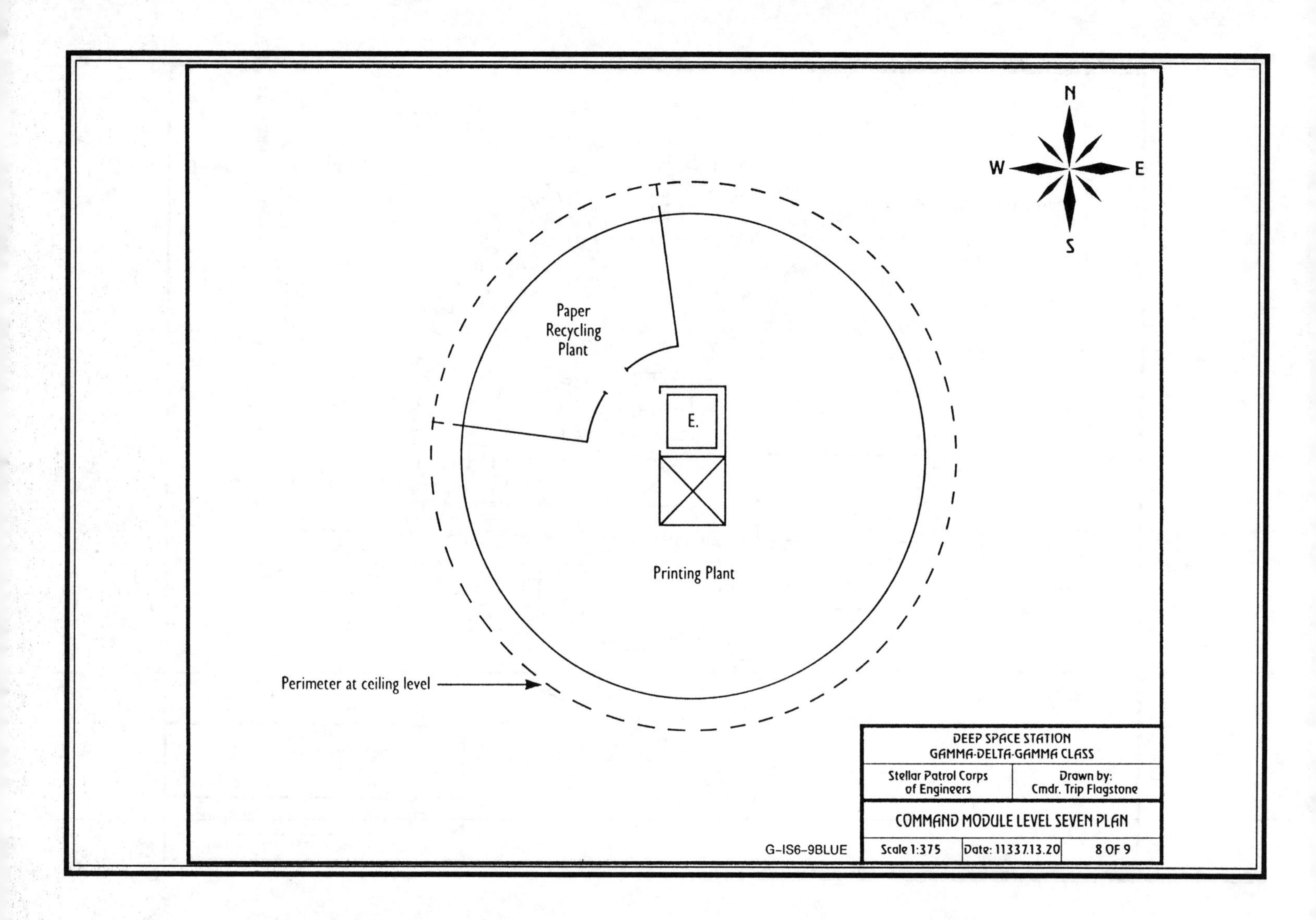
N
W
E
S
Paper
Recycling
Plant
E.
Printing Plant
Perimeter at ceiling level
DEEP SPACE STATION
GAMMA-DELTA-GAMMA CLASS
Stellar Patrol Corps
of Engineers
Drawn by:
Cmdr. Trip Flagstone
COMMAND MODULE LEVEL SEVEN PLAN
G-IS6-9BLUE
Scale 1:375
Date: 11337.13.20
8 OF 9

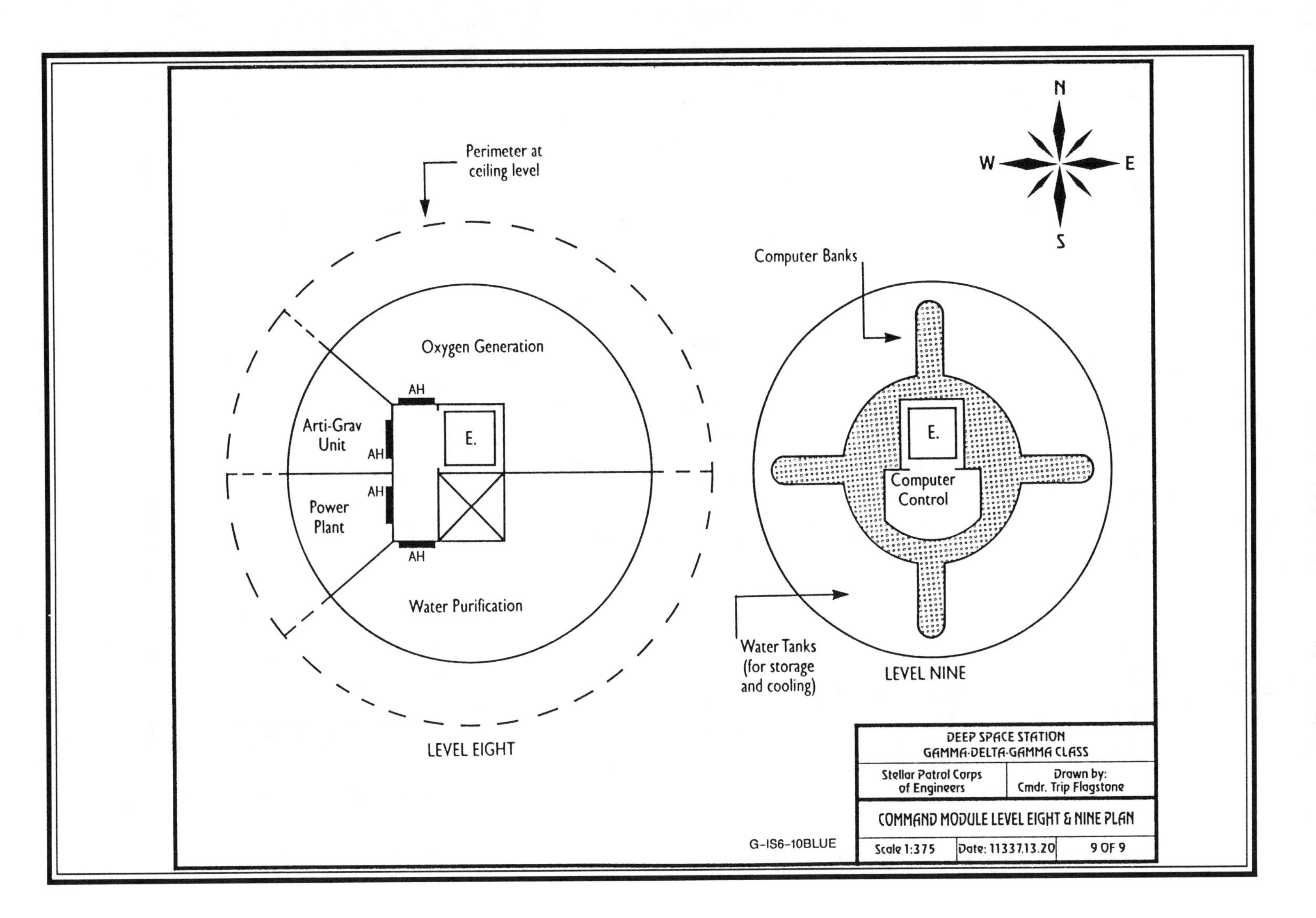
N
W
E
S
Perimeter at
ceiling level
Oxygen Generation
AH
E.
Arti-Grav
Unit
AH
AH
Power
Plant
AH
Water Purification
LEVEL EIGHT
Computer Banks
E.
Computer
Control
Water Tanks
(for storage
and cooling)
LEVEL NINE
DEEP SPACE STATION
GAMMA-DELTA-GAMMA CLASS
Stellar Patrol Corps
of Engineers
Drawn by:
Cmdr. Trip Flagstone
COMMAND MODULE LEVEL EIGHT & NINE PLAN
G-IS6-10BLUE
Scale 1:375
Date: 11337.13.20
9 OF 9

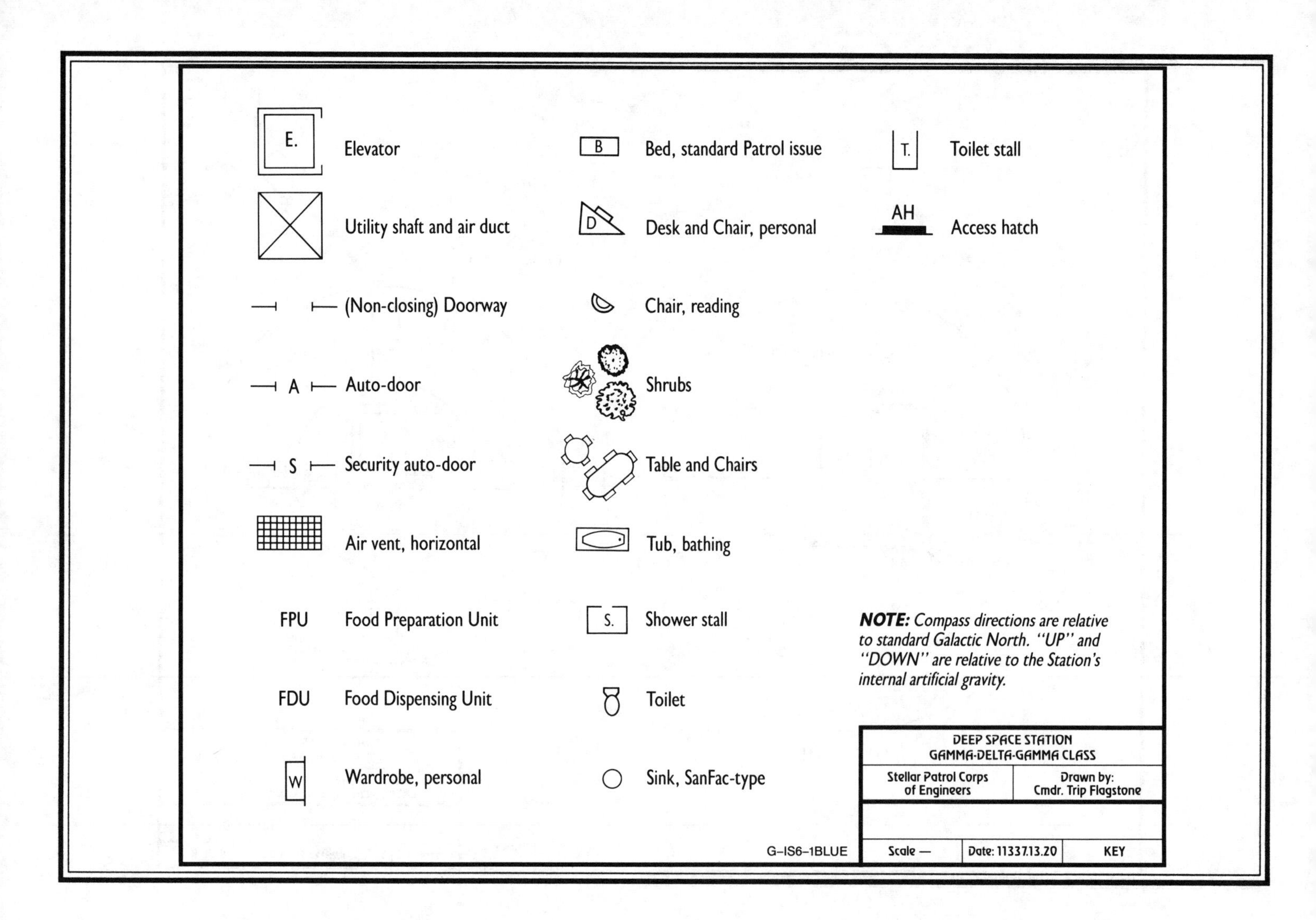
E.
Elevator
Utility shaft and air duct
(Non-closing) Doorway
A
Auto-door
S
Security auto-door
Air vent, horizontal
FPU
Food Preparation Unit
FDU
Food Dispensing Unit
W
Wardrobe, personal
B
Bed, standard Patrol issue
D
Desk and Chair, personal
Chair, reading
Shrubs
Table and Chairs
Tub, bathing
S.
Shower stall
Toilet
Sink, SanFac-type
T.
Toilet stall
AH
Access hatch
NOTE: Compass directions are relative to standard Galactic North. "UP" and "DOWN" are relative to the Station's internal artificial gravity.
DEEP SPACE STATION
GAMMA-DELTA-GAMMA CLASS
Stellar Patrol Corps of Engineers
Drawn by: Cmdr. Trip Flagstone
G–IS6–1BLUE
Scale —
Date: 11337.13.20
KEY

# Suspended

Preface to the Story

You are the Central Mentality on an advanced semi-automated planet. You were supposed to sleep — in limited cryogenic suspension — for the next 500 years, 20 miles beneath the surface of the planet, while the great Filtering Computers maintained all surface systems. But the computers have taken you out of suspension because something is terribly wrong: the weather has become brutal, food production is dangerously low, and the Transportation System is malfunctioning, causing unprecedented accidents and casualties. The planet is in chaos. You yourself cannot move. But you have six robots at your disposal, and you must manipulate them strategically to bring the Filtering Computers back into balance. Each robot has a distinct perception of the world and offers you specific abilities — one offers you sight, a second hearing, a third access to information in the computer memory bank Through the robots, you must save the planet from destruction.

**Be sure to use the "Underground Complex" Schematic in the Map packet included in "The Lost Treasure" box.**

About the Author

Michael Berlyn is a writer whose books include The Integrated Man and Crystal Phoenix from Bantam Books. He is the author of SUS-PENDED, INFIDEL, and CUTTHROATS, all from Infocom.

# Briefing for the Contra Central Mentality

LOTT57-71234-6198

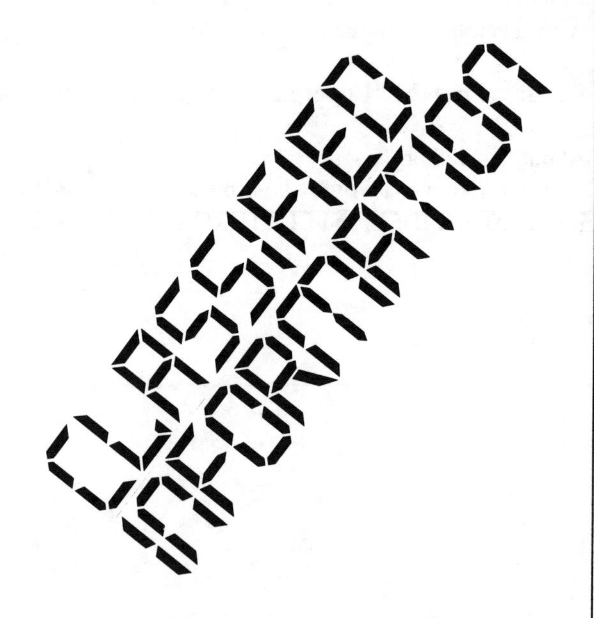

Occupant/Subcluster B93000
Sector 12, Contra SW RP35/34412.8

Congratulations. You have been chosen as the winner of the semi-millennial Lottery, and as such will have the honor of serving as Contra's Central Mentality for the next 500 years.

Naturally, this title brings with it certain responsibilities, not the least of which is ensuring the survival of life on this planet. To this end, in accordance with Procedural Substatute 2.5X:845A77b, you will be placed in a state of limited cryogenic suspension. In this sleep-like mode, your mind will monitor the Filtering Computers that maintain the delicate balance of our surface-side systems. Should an emergency occur which causes a Filtering Computer imbalance, you will be awakened. It will then be up to you to ascertain the problem and perform such remedial actions as you deem necessary. The penalties for failure are all too obvious.

A briefing has been prepared to familiarize you with your duties in your new role. It has been revised and amended to enable you to avoid the tragic errors of your predecessor, the lamentable Gregory Franklin. The briefing supersedes and countermands all previous briefings issued by the Lottery Commission.

It may be material at this time to review the Franklin Incident. The report of the events appearing in the Contra Citizen of two months ago, while editorial in nature, sums up the circumstances succinctly:

"...but Franklin was not destined to complete his tour of duty. After 467 years, he awoke by mistake, and, not being extremely bright to start with, lost what little sense and sanity he had. He looked around the Underground Complex for an emergency, found none and decided to create one of his own.

"Overriding the three Filtering Computers, he directed the transportation systems to kill whoever happened to be walking outside or riding on any of the glide ramps. Psychologists believe that he must have possessed a twisted sense of humor—to have people maimed, run over, chased by robot-taxis provided him with pleasure for the moment. However, he soon tired of this and decided to eliminate a larger section of the population in a far easier manner.

"Ever since weather had been controlled, dwellings had not been designed to withstand snow and sleet. Franklin altered the pressure in the Weather Towers near the cities, setting off raging storms and creating freezing temperatures. Thousands perished from exposure; thousands more became popsicles.

"The surviving authorities decided to send an extermination squad down into the Underground Complex to remove Franklin from his suspension capsule. They got there just in time. When they arrived, Franklin had the six maintenance robots snipping wires and causing havoc with the Filtering Computers and automated systems.

"In the tragedy's aftermath, several known malcontents protested that the system had proven itself infeasible; these complaints were dealt with summarily by the Authority, which assures all citizens that new improvements in the system and the method for selecting future central mentalities have eliminated any cause for alarm..."

With this in mind, you can well understand why the Authority insists on a comprehensive briefing before you enter the Complex. You are therefore requested to read the enclosed briefing with the greatest care before entering the suspended state.

Ignatz Feroukin

Ignatz Feroukin
VP/Memos

Addendum: The Office of Cloning and Personnel Development informs us that a number of replicates of you are currently under production, for use in the event that we find it necessary to remove you. This should in no way be construed as a reflection on you as a person; despite the fact that your psychological profile revealed a few characteristics which could be termed "deviant," we have only the highest expectations for you. Needless to say, however, the Authority desires no repeats of Franklin's performance. Therefore, remember: you can be replaced.

Lottery Commission Headquarters, Bureau of Awards & Prizes, Contra Central, XR27/55693.1

# Briefing for the Contra Central Mentality

## CLASSIFIED

This briefing has been updated and revised many times to ensure accuracy and completeness. In a crisis, our planet's survival depends on you. We cannot overstate the importance of the information contained herein.

Since Contra was terraformed and settled by emigres from Earth, we have had the benefit of living within a controlled environment. As you well know, our weather is always perfect and there is food for everyone—wholesome, delicious food. Anyone wishing to travel the surface of our planet simply takes a glide ramp, a robot-taxi, or a floater.

This controlled and balanced environment is maintained by three massive and powerful computers buried deep beneath Contra's surface. Without these computers, we would be forced to brave the elemental fury of Contra and provide for ourselves using primitive methods and skills.

Contra's three Filtering Computers maintain and monitor all surface-side systems.

## YOUR RESPONSIBILITIES TO CONTRA

Since these three Filtering Computers are biomechanical in construction, they must be monitored. It is the duty of the Central Mentality to monitor these Filtering Computers to ensure they function properly.

The Filtering Computers are located in an extremely high-security area called the Underground Complex. With one exception, monitoring of the Filtering Computers has always proceeded without trouble. Since training and costs prohibit frequent changing of the Central Mentality, you will be in the Complex for 500 years.

Your time in the Complex will be spent in a state of limited cryogenic suspension. You will be frozen to nearly absolute zero and then stored in a cryogenic capsule within the Complex. Your brain will remain in an Alpha state, receptive but quiet, requiring only minimal biological functions. You will be able to survive in this state for your tour of duty: 500 years.

## IF SOMETHING GOES WRONG

It won't. But if it does, the computers responsible for all of our surface-side systems will awaken you and inform you of the problem. We are confident you will be capable of solving any situations which may arise. The fate of the entire population of Contra will rest in your abilities to make logical decisions and choices.

Your body will be warmed to the point where marginal biological activity is resumed, supplying your mind with the necessary nutrients and oxygen to function at peak capacity. Unfortunately, we cannot revive you completely until the end of your tour of duty.

Due to the Gregory Franklin incident (refer to the letter from the Lottery Commission), we are forced to make clones of you. When you complete this briefing, the cloning procedure will begin. These clones will be installed in the Complex as a backup system, should anything go wrong with you.

# THE UNDERGROUND COMPLEX

The Underground Complex you will occupy is fully automated and maintained by six robots. In the unlikely event that the Filtering Computers malfunction, there are override controls for the weather systems, the transit systems and the hydroponics food resource center. There are also planet-side monitors for examining the current state of these systems.

The robots which maintain the Complex are under the control of the Filtering Computers. Malfunctioning equipment is quickly and easily detected by the computers themselves, and the necessary robots are dispatched to effect the replacements. If you are ever awakened (an extremely unlikely event), robots will provide your link to the outside world.

# THE SIX ROBOTS

The most recent facilities check indicates that your robotic crew is fully operational (with the exception noted below). The following profiles have been provided to inform you of special capabilities of individual robots, so that you can make the best use of each member of your crew, should corrective maneuvers become necessary.

**Iris** is a visual robot whose mobility is limited. Her ability to describe things approaches what a human being might see in most circumstances. Since the Frobozz Engineering Company was responsible for her design and construction, she has limited abilities for grasping, carrying, etc., and has only two grasping extensions. An historical note: she proved to be the butt of many design and implementation jokes on Contra's surface, one of which was "The eyes have it." Humor of this sort has, of course, since been outlawed on Contra.

Iris's limited mobility results from her complex optical capabilities. Due to these abilities, only a limited mapping of the Complex was included in her logic circuits. This design restriction allows Iris to wander about the areas only in which she serves a useful purpose.

**Waldo** is an industrious robot. Since his primary purpose is to manipulate objects, he has been provided with six grasping extensions. He travels by using a sonar-feedback mechanism and, when close to or touching an object, can detect quite a bit about its inherent characteristics based on this sonar. In addition, he has a highly developed sense of touch and can prove to be a delicate workman.

**Sensa** is a peculiar mixture of sensory apparatuses. She can detect vibrational activity, photon emission sources and ionic discharges. She is also rigged to automatically perform such sensory tasks as the analysis of diffraction indexes. Sensa has five extensions, two of which are used exclusively for sensory input. The other three extensions are grasping extensions.

**Auda** is all ears, capable of processing and interpreting auditory signals within the Complex. Her presence is required by the CLU (Consolidated Listeners Union), and though Auda may not be very helpful in the high-tech sense, in case of human intervention she is absolutely essential. Auda has but one grasping extension.

**Poet** is a peculiar robot whose function was somehow altered over time by the Filtering Computers. Poet was originally intended as a diagnostic robot. He has been equipped with a diagnostic sensor which is activated when he has been directed to TOUCH something. Unless Poet is actually doing his thing, he makes the best of what he perceives, translating his input into occasionally bewildering output. Despite the sometimes seeming lack of sense to his statements, they provide an accurate representation of reality. In addition to his "touching" extension, Poet has been provided with three grasping extensions.

**Whiz** is an interfacing device between you and the Central Library Core, a huge data bank available to your queries. Whiz can PLUG IN to any of the four CLC peripherals and find information for you. This information pertains to objects and the Complex in general. The CLC contains no information about any of the rooms your robots can visit. Although Whiz is extremely helpful, he does have his limitations. There was once a robot-joke about Whiz being a real airhead; if he could have understood it, he would have taken offense. Whiz has two grasping extensions.

**Note:** There is a seventh robot. Standing almost two meters tall and featuring 16 grasping extensions, verbal circuits and heavy-duty shielding against acid damage, this model is optimized for a multitude of applications. It should be mentioned that this robot was misused by Gregory Franklin, who abandoned it within the Complex after brutally mangling it beyond recognition or hope of repair.

# THE CENTRAL LIBRARY CORE (CLC)

**The Central Library Core (CLC)** is composed of several distinct parts: Whiz, the Peripherals and the Library Core.

**Whiz.** Whiz's function with the CLC is to act as your querying device. By plugging him in, you can ask questions about objects and get advice on situations.

**The Peripherals.** There are four peripherals accessible to Whiz:

The Index Peripheral—Querying this peripheral performs the following operations: The object is passed along to the Central Language Core, at which point its name is matched against an index. If the name is not found, you will be informed that the object is not on file and no peripheral will contain any reference to it. If the object is found within the Language Core, it is passed to the Index Core. The Index Core then scans through the tagging device for references. If no references are found, you will be told that no data is available at any peripheral. If references are found, you will be told at which peripherals information can be retrieved.

The Technical Peripheral—This peripheral can provide technical data on some objects. If you absolutely need to know how something works, querying this peripheral can sometimes prove helpful. Technical information is not available on all objects.

The Advisory Peripheral—When you need advice and just can't understand what's going on with something, ask this peripheral. It is attuned to provide Hierarchical Information for Newly Terraformed Systems (H.I.N.T.S.).

The Historical Peripheral—This peripheral can provide you with historical references for certain objects found within the Complex, adding a greater understanding of what these things do and how they interact.

**The Library Core.** The CLC itself is also accessible from the Lower Access area, but all interactions and queries here are designed solely for human interaction. Whiz cannot perform queries from this area since there isn't a suitable peripheral for him.

# THE SURFACE SYSTEMS

The surface of Contra is controlled by the three Filtering Computers. These systems, when in proper balance, maintain the weather, the transportation systems and the food production automatically. By polling surface-side peripherals, the Filtering Computers can make decisions on what adjustments are necessary for a balanced environment. If the Filtering Computers cannot mutually agree on a course of action, you will be awakened to make the necessary decisions.

**The Weather System.** Weather on the surface of Contra is controlled by Weather Towers. Each city has three towers which control atmospheric pressure within the surrounding area. By testing temperature, wind velocity and relative humidity, the three Filtering Computers can make adjustments in the Weather Towers to maintain a balanced, comfortable state. Since the weather on the surface is controlled, housing and clothing are more decorative than protective, and maintaining a balanced weather condition becomes a primary concern.

Since the planetary engineers were aware of this; they built the Weather Monitors and the Weather Controls into the Complex. You have been provided with manual override controls in case the Filtering Computers fall out of synchronization and cannot agree on a course of action. These controls are found in the Weather Control Area and consist of three dials, each of which controls a set of towers in all the cities of Contra. The first dial, for example, controls the pressure in all of the first towers in all of the cities.

The Weather Monitors provide you with the necessary feedback on the planet's surface so that you can make necessary adjustments.

**Food Production.** Food is produced hydroponically deep underground, separated from the Underground Complex by nearly half a planet. The Filtering Computers prepare and balance the amount of water, minerals and light for the Hydroponic Growing Area. This area is not accessible to you or the robots because of its distant location, but you do have manual control over it, should the need ever arise.

The Hydroponic Monitors provide you with a continual analysis of the Growing Area, while three levers in the Hydroponic Control Area allow you to manually override the three Filtering Computers' settings.

**The Transportation System.** Transportation on Contra's surface is totally automated and controlled by the Filtering Computers. There are three basic forms of transportation: floaters, taxis and glide ramps.

Floaters are small single- or double-occupant bubbles which travel through the air. They travel on lines of force, generated from the ground, maintained and controlled by the Filtering Computers. Collisions are normally unheard of, and not a single casualty has ever occurred due to traffic problems. The Transit Monitors tell you how many floaters are currently in use, while a manual override switch is located in the Transit Control Area. By turning off the switch, you can turn off the lines of force to the floaters.

The taxis are actually robots, semi-intelligent vehicles which are guided by the Filtering Computers. They have on-board power, so the manual override system, a switch in the Transit Control Area, instructs the taxis to stop picking up passengers rather than simply shutting them off. (When Franklin was in control, he managed to figure out a method of getting the Filtering Computers out of balance, causing the taxis to seek out pedestrians and run them down.)

The glide ramps are similar in function to conveyor belts, transporting the bulk of the population at a leisurely pace. The ramps are speed-controlled by the Filtering Computers and can be shut off by using the manual override switch located in the Transit Control area.

**A Final Note.** Your 500-year tour of duty will indubitably fly by trouble-free. Pleasant dreams.

# Starcross

Preface to the Story

The year is 2186. Humanity has established colonies on the Moon, Mars, and several of the larger asteroids. Earth's sky is dotted with space habitats, and the spaceways are always busy. As usual, there is the urgent need for energy to power this advanced civilization; one of the primary sources of that energy is quantum black holes. In STARCROSS, you are a black hole miner, scouring the asteroid belt in your one-man survey ship. Finding and harnessing a single black hole can make a person's fortune. It's a lonely business, fraught with the known and unknown hazards of space. You've equipped your ship, the mining vessel Starcross, with the best gear you could afford. You've put everything into this venture, and though you've tried before, you somehow sense that this time will be different. The ship's computer handles the functions of navigation and routine maintenance. You watch the sophisticated mass detector as it unceasingly scans the vicinity for uncharted masses. To assuage the tedium of your long trip, you browse through the compact tape library, a compendium of human knowledge and culture. But the drone of the ship gradually lulls you into a deep sleep. As you sleep, you dream of the riches which would be yours if your search for a quantum black hole is successful. Little do you suspect that the ala your mass detector is about to jolt you out of your dream - but not to grapple with the long-sought black hole. Your quest has taken an unexpected turn, for you are destined to rendezvous with a gargantuan alien spaceship from the outer fringes of the galaxy.

About the Author

Dave Lebling was born in Washington, D. C. and grew up in suburban Maryland. He attended the Massachusetts Institute of Technology, and worked at MIT's Laboratory for Computer Science, where he developed an interest in computer entertainments. He was a co-author of the original mainframe Zork. He has co-authored Zork I, Zork II, Zork III, and Enchanter, and written Starcross and Suspect on his own

# BUREAU OF EXTRA-SOLAR INTELLIGENCE

TO: All Spacecraft Owners and Operators
FROM: Bureau of Extra-Solar Intelligence
SUBJECT: Encounters with Aliens
DATE: February 8, 2132

As of this writing, no registered spacecrafts have documented any encounters with alien life forms. Although sightings of unidentified objects have been reported, none have proved reliable.

Nevertheless, this Bureau believes that alien life forms do exist and will enter our solar system within the next millennium. This belief is based in part on the fact that repetitious signals have been received at the Arecibo and Pulkovo observatory dishes since the late twentieth century. The source of these signals—seven dashes followed by either three or 11 dashes—has not been established, but clearly a highly advanced civilization is sending them.

Should you or any of your crew members have an encounter with any alien life form, notify your local space safety patrol as soon as possible. Extensive research suggests that there is a 99 percent chance that an alien will have only peaceful intentions. Do not—repeat, DO NOT—hurt or kill any alien unless it is a life-or-death situation for you or a member of your crew.

We have surmised that any alien will be equipped with sensory organs, physical manipulators, a method of locomotion, and a method for gathering energy and eliminating waste heat and (most likely) chemicals. Note that alien life forms are likely to have evolved under extremely different conditions than have existed on Earth. They may not be able to perceive the same physical and electromagnetic frequencies as humans. They may not consist of a carbon-based chemistry, and their metabolisms may not be chemical in nature. The atmosphere of your ship may be poisonous to them, and vice versa.

It is possible that an alien race will be similar to ours in appearance. However, do not let appearances fool you; gestures and facial expressions are cultural in origin and are likely to mean different things. A smile, for instance, may be interpreted as a baring of teeth, forewarning attack. If you do encounter an alien, please remain calm and be very careful. Remember: the first alien encounter will be an historic event far surpassing Columbus's discovery of America. The responsibility of being ambassador for all Earth is very great, but the rewards for success will be greater.

LOG OF THE M.C.S.

# STARCROSS™

**Registered out of Ceres**
**Registration 47291AA-4X**

Constructed in 2178, Luna City Docks

**M.C.S. STARCROSS 02-28-2186**

First entry in the new log! Finally got the loans to finance the purchasing of my own mining ship. They were a little reluctant about it at first, what with me never having actually found a black hole. That is, never having found one that didn't already belong to someone else, to put the best light on it. I think the terms were a little steep: after all, I'll pay them back. They didn't have to reserve the right to grow a clone to work for them for "20 years and a day." Bankers are *so* conservative. I suppose that's to be expected from computers. I'm not prejudiced; some of my best friends are programmed.

Once I got a loan, I took possession of the STARCROSS. A sweet little ship. Only eight years old, been on only three previous mining trips. The guy at Wheat City Used Transportation said the previous owner was a nice little old lady who retired after her last trip—she found a 1.5 gigawatt black hole out near Saturn, of all places! I knew then it was a lucky ship.

**M.C.S. STARCROSS 03-04-2186**

Not too much difficulty getting the ship moved to Ceres Spaceport. Of course, the hauler didn't show up on time, but that's what you'd expect.

The ship is well equipped for the money. I kept most of the program modules in the ship's computer and updated only a few of them. I got the inertial guidance overhauled and checked out the mass detector myself. I wish I could afford the I/O options to have a fully integrated system. Blast off tomorrow!

**M.C.S. STARCROSS 03-05-2186**

Got underway a little late, due to a problem in the fuel tanks. I spent the time stocking up on new entertainment tapes—some really nice ones, too, but kind of expensive. So much time prospecting is spent waiting for something to happen.

**M.C.S. STARCROSS 03-28-2186**

Underway less than four weeks and I'm about to go crazy! First, the entertainment tapes were mislabelled. It's all highbrow stuff like operas and lectures. *Leather Goddesses of Phobos* was really something about the history of the Terran Union. What a rip-off! I suppose I can always talk to the computer.

I can't stand those tapes. I'll save them for later in the voyage when I'm really desperate. I'll play games with the computer to keep amused that way.

**M.C.S. STARCROSS 04-02-2186**

I'm tempted to dismantle the computer. First, instead of a smooth, chummy voice, it sounds like a uranium recycler that's dropped a critical mass on its grasping extensors. Well, maybe it's not that bad, but it's really surly. Insubordinate, too. I tried playing chess with it, but it was too good and made lots of nasty comments about my pawn structure. So I told it to play on an easier level, and it refused! It said it was boring enough playing a human without giving away the game.

**M.C.S. STARCROSS 04-15-2186**

Possible black hole today! The mass detector went off. The alarm is really loud and practically sent me through the bulkhead. Even the computer complained about it, but you can't turn it down.

Anyway, it looks like a big mass; at a good area, too—near the trailing Trojan point of Jupiter. Hasn't been prospected out yet, and there's always something new there thanks to Jupe's big mass.

Off we go!

**M.C.S. STARCROSS 04-16-2186**

Turns out it was just a nickel-iron asteroid. It was a pretty big one, but with Asian Steel mining at full capacity, there's no room for the little guy. Their margin is tiny per ton, and they can bring back really big chunks.

In fact, when I got closer to the asteroid, I discovered it had an Asian Steel transponder on it already. The computer said it knew it was nickel-iron all along, but I think it's just putting on airs.

**M.C.S. STARCROSS 05-12-2186**

Another false alarm. This one was nickel-iron, too.

**M.C.S. STARCROSS 05-23-2186**

Finally beat the computer at chess! A really neat combination, too. What a poor sport! It says I cheated and won't talk to me anymore.

**M.C.S. STARCROSS 05-29-2186**

Computer still not talking to me, beyond accepting routine ship commands. Even then it sounds particularly sullen. In the meantime, I've invented 11 new forms of five-suit solitaire. Unfortunately, I haven't won any of them yet.

**M.C.S. STARCROSS 05-30-2186**

Another asteroid. This one is mostly uranium. Gives a big blip on the mass detector, it's so heavy. Probably ought to mark it for removal. The Patrol will be pleased, even if the reward isn't commensurate. I could try smuggling it to the Ganymedean Insurgents, but the penalty for being caught with unlicensed uranium is 20 years on an organ farm. I'd prefer to have my original kidneys until they wear out, thank you.

**M.C.S. STARCROSS 06-11-2186**

A micro-meteorite pierced the hull today! It was pretty exciting, but I fixed it like a pro. I had to put on my suit, get out the patch kit and patch the bulkhead. The hole was almost big enough to put my finger in! The patch looks like a big wad of chewing gum, but it gets really hard.

Happy to report that after I repressurized, the computer started talking to me again. Mostly insults, but better than nothing.

**M.C.S. STARCROSS 06-23-2186**

I found a black hole for real today!

Unfortunately, someone else's transponder started up about two hours ago, and now he's warning me off in no uncertain terms.

That does it. I'm going to try something really different. Too many prospectors around here. Nobody prospects in the inner system anymore, but I will, and my luck's going to change!

In toward Mars!

# M. C. S. STARCROSS

MASS DETECTOR OUTPUT
TIME - 2186 : 104 : 58923
VALID UNTIL - 2186 : 104 : 59287

**Legend**
R = Range
Θ = Theta
Φ = Phi

Keep Space Beautiful

Use Your Trash Atomizer

UNCHARTED MASS COORDINATES

| Name | R | Θ | Φ |
|---|---|---|---|
| UM08 | 150 | : 110 | : 017° |
| UM12 | 100 | : 345 | : 107° |
| UM24 | 100 | : 285 | : 087° |
| UM28 | 250 | : 45 | : 178° |
| UM31 | 150 | : 105 | : 067° |
| UM52 | 175 | : 165 | : 035° |
| UM70 | 100 | : 135 | : 101° |
| UM91 | 50 | : 15 | : 121° |

ASTEROID CORRDINATES

| Name | R | Θ | Φ |
|---|---|---|---|
| AX01 | 200 | : 240 | : 134° |
| AX32 | 125 | : 240 | : 105° |
| AX71 | 125 | : 180 | : 047° |
| AX87 | 125 | : 75 | : 102° |

INHABITED ASTEROID CORRDINATES

| Name | R | Θ | Φ |
|---|---|---|---|
| AB40 | 250 | : 300 | : 022° |

SHIP CORRDINATES

| Name | R | Θ | Φ |
|---|---|---|---|
| US75 | 175 | : 135 | : 034° |

INSTRUCTIONS FOR USE:
TO REACH YOUR DESTINATION, ENTER THE THREE CORRDINATES INTO YOUR NAVIGATION COMPUTER BY TYPING:
**COMPUTER, RANGE IS (VALUE). THETA IS (VALUE). PHI IS (VALUE).**
AS A SAFETY FEATURE, YOUR COMPUTER WILL NOT INITATE A NEW NAVIGATIONAL PROGRAM WITHOUT CONFIRMATION. YOU CAN DO THIS BY TYPING:
**COMPUTER, CONFIRM NEW COURSE.**

# Hitchhiker's Guide to the Galaxy

Preface to the Story

Don't Panic! Relax, because everything you need to know about playing The Hitchhiker's Guide to the Galaxy is contained in the pages of this manual. In this story, you will be Arthur Dent, a rather ordinary earth creature who gets swept up in a whirlwind of interstellar adventures almost beyond comprehension. As the story begins bulldozers are waiting to reduce your house to rubble to make way for a motorway bypass. While you attempt to deal with this problem, your rather strange friend Ford Prefect drops by to tell you that the Earth is about to be demolished to make way for an interstellar bypass! If you survive this double threat, you'll embark on a series of inter-galactic misadventures even funnier than your worst nightmares! And, because anything is possible in The Hitchhiker's Guide to the Galaxy, you may soon not even be sure of your own identity! A special note for people who have read the book "The Hitchhiker's Guide to the Galaxy" Although the opening of the game is fairly similar to the book, the story quickly diverges, with lots of new material and different twists. Although familiarity with the story may make a few of the early puzzles easier, if you rely too heavily on this previous knowledge you will certainly end up getting misled.

About the Authors

Douglas Adams graduated from Cambridge in 1974, where he was an active member of the Footlights Club, which has launched the careers of many of Britain's great comics. He has collaborated on several projects with Monty Python's Graham Chapman, and has served as a writer and script editor for the TV series "Dr. Who." THE HITCHHIKER'S GUIDE TO THE GALAXY began in 1978 as a BBC radio serial, and its popularity soon propelled it into four books, a television series, two records, and a stage show.

Steve Meretzky (1957- ) was born and raised in Yonkers, NY, where his early hobbies included rooting for the New York Mets and against Richard Nixon. A few historians of interactive fiction think that Meretzky's first job, packing nuts and bolts for his father's hardware business, was the formative moment of his writing career. A few other people think that there's absolutely no connection. Most people don't think about it at all. Along with Infocom's Dave Lebling, Meretzky is the first person admitted to the Science Fiction Writers of America for authoring interactive fiction.

## Hitchhiker's Guide to the Galaxy Special Commands

*FOOTNOTE - Occasionally the text in Hitchhiker's will mention the existence of a footnote. To read the footnote, simply type FOOTNOTE followed by the appropriate footnote number (for example, FOOTNOTE 2) This will not count as a turn.

*HINT - If you have difficulty while playing the game, and you can't figure out what to do, just type HINT. Then follow the directions at the top of your screen to read the hint of your choice.

# YES! THE UNIVERSE CAN BE YOURS FOR LESS THAN 30 ALTAIRIAN DOLLARS PER DAY!

**BLACK HOLES. SAVAGE ALIEN WARRIOR TRIBES.** Welfare planets ruled by dry-cleaning establishments, where even the most basic of human necessities are provided for a day late and with too much starch. Face it, the Universe is **NO PLACE TO TRY AND HAVE A GOOD TIME.**

Unless, that is, you're the proud owner of that wholly remarkable object, *The Hitchhiker's Guide to the Galaxy*!

Within the million-plus pages of *The Guide*, which in many corners of the Galaxy has already supplanted the *Encyclopedia Galactica* as the standard repository of all knowledge and wisdom, you'll find **EVERYTHING YOU NEED TO KNOW** about the Universe, from the utmost trivia to the most vital information pertaining to your health and well-being. **WE UNCONDITIONALLY GUARANTEE** it will teach you how to survive and even **ENJOY THE UNIVERSE—ALL ON ONLY 30 ALTAIRIAN DOLLARS PER DAY!*** Just take a peek at this mere sample of *The Guide*'s **MILLIONS OF USES** and, like so many other satisfied customers, you'll be convinced that this is truly **THE MOST WHOLLY REMARKABLE ITEM YOU'LL EVER BUY!**

**PLANNING A HONEYMOON?** Let *The Guide* show you how to get the best rates and accommodations on exclusive vacation paradises like Vortaqua,planet of the Heart-Shaped Hot Tub Lakes!

**TRIVIA BUFF?** *The Guide* has all the answers,as well as most of the questions. For example: What titles comprise Oolon Colluphid's trilogyof philo-sophical blockbusters?

*Answer: Where God Went Wrong, Some Moreof God's Greatest Mistakes and Who Is This God Person, Anyway?*

**CONVENTION COMING UP?** *The Guide* knows where to find all the swankiest hotels, the trendiest restaurants, the swingingest nightclubs, the friendliest escort services and the cheapest duty-free shops in which to buy gifts for appeasing one's family and conscience!

**NEED HELP FAST?** In a flash, *The Guide* can supply you with such useful tidbits of information as: how to tell your Aunt Clara from a Seven-Stomached Gorba Plant; what to do if Aunt Clara has been devoured by a Seven-Stomached Gorba Plant; how to perform the Heimlich Maneuver on a Seven-Stomached Gorba Plant, and much, much more!

*"30 Altarian Dollars Per Day" is an estimated figure and is provided strictly for purposes of comparison. Actual expenses may be higher.**
**In fact, we're sure of it. Quite frankly, if you're not absolutely prepared to lie, cheat, steal your food, pass rubber checks to unsuspecting hotel clerks, hoodwink customs officials, forge passports en-titling you to diplomatic immunity, utilize bogus student and/or elderly identification cards to get yourself into tourist attractions at reduced rates, stiff everyone possible on tips and otherwise make a mockery of Intergalactic Law, just about the only way you're going to get by on 30 Altairians per diem is by staying home and camping out in your own backyard.

# AND THAT'S NOT ALL!

*The Guide* is more than a super travelogue or an incredible answer machine—it's a lovely addition to any backpack or suitcase that fits in perfectly with every decor. It comes in a wrinkle-proof, scratch-resistant plastic cover with **THE LOOK AND FEEL OF REAL VINYL**, handsomely inscribed with the words **DON'T PANIC** in large, friendly letters. And talk about handy—The **Mark IV** version of *The Guide* has **MORE OPTIONS THAN A 20-ARMED HRUGMUS HAS HANGNAILS!** Just look what you can get...

**73-FUNCTION POCKET CALCULATOR OPTION** lets you solve equations that have baffled mathematicians for eons, such as how to travel faster than the speed of light without losing your luggage.

**CUSTOM CHRONOMETER** displays year, month, day and date, to within a fraction of a sluub in civilian time *and* military time *and* Happy Hour Time for the nearest pub in the Galaxy.

**TAN-O-MATIC REFERENCE TABLE** tells you the exact coordinates of all the best beaches, the most up-to-date fashion tips on polarized eyewear and reflectors, the precise length of time you can sunbathe before your friends have to carry you home in an urn, and the appropriate level of sunscreen to wear in case of a supernova.

**SIRIUS CYBERNETICS BAROMETER/ NEO-DESCARTIAN RELATIVE TRUTH MONITOR** indicates temperature, barometric pressure, high tide, low tide, wind direction and velocity, prevailing weather conditions, amount of precipitation in the last 1,000 sluubs and whether you're actually experiencing any of it or are simply being deceived by your imperfect senses.

**SALAD-SLASHER/FOOD PROCESSOR/ LEMON ZESTER ATTACHMENT** slices, dices, chops and bludgeons even the most rubbery fruit or vegetable in seconds!

# BUT WAIT...

# THERE'S MORE!

Now for a **LIMITED TIME ONLY** when you **RUSH** your *Hitchhiker's Guide to the Galaxy* order to Megadodo Publications, you'll also get as our **SPECIAL GIFT** to you **ENOUGH THROW-IN ITEMS TO FILL AN ATTIC!** So act now and receive all these fabulous bonuses!

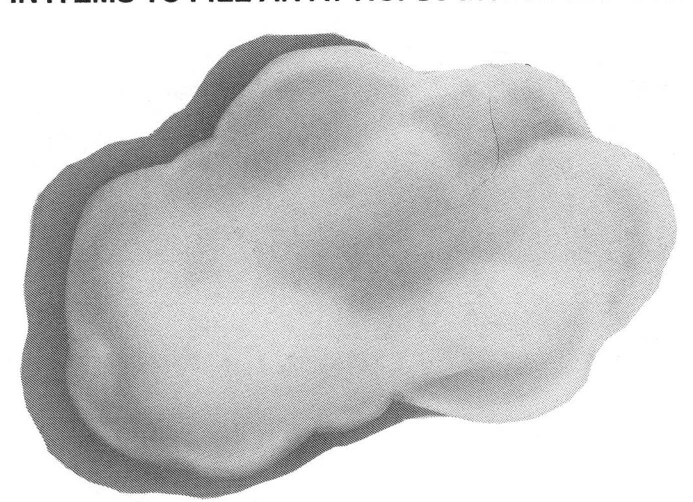

**FLUFF:** Goes anywhere—under the bed, behind the commode, at the bottom of your pocket, inside your navel!

## DESTRUCT ORDERS FOR YOUR HOME AND PLANET:

Suitable for framing, and great gag gifts at any party!

ORDER FOR DESTRUCTION

Be it known that on this day the 4 th day of October in the Year of Our Lord 1982 that by decree of the Domicile Demolition Department of Cottingshire County, the residence of Arthur Dent at 155 Country Lane in the town of Cottington shall herewith be demolished, destroyed and otherwise transformed into a nondescript heap of pulverized rubble, said resident(s) having evacuated said premises within 750 days of the issuance of this document; this order to be carried out regardless of acknowledgement by said resident(s) of proper notification, said demolition being necessitated by reason of

(Check one)
- National emergency.
- Health hazard.
- Complex technical matters.
- ✓ It's in the way.

Said property has been seized by Right of Eminent Domain for future use as:

(Check one)
- ✓ Highway right-of-way
- Parking facilities
- Shopping mall.
- Wildlife sanctuary.
- Hunting grounds
- New offices for Domicile Demolition Department.
- Vacant lot.
- Other (please specify):

DOMICILE DEMOLITION DEPARTMENT

We the undersigned do hereby authorise the execution of this order through the powers vested in us by the State. God Save the Queen!

Commissioner, Domicile Demolition Department

Vice Commissioner, Domicile Demolition Department

Earle of Cottingshire

Copy A: For Issuance to Resident(s)

**DON'T PANIC! BUTTON:** Perfect for those times when your planet is being bombarded by laser beams, your toaster starts talking to you and traces of radioactivity are discovered in your breakfast cereal!

**JOO JANTA 200
SUPER-CHROMATIC
PERIL-SENSITIVE SUNGLASSES:** ****
You'll look cool and stay cool even when attending a Vogon poetry reading!

**NO TEA:** Just like the tea professional hitchhikers don't carry!

**MICROSCOPIC SPACE FLEET:** Just the thing for attacking microscopic civilizations.

**** Not recommended for driving.

# HOW MUCH WOULD YOU PAY NOW? ONE HUNDRED ALTAIRIAN DOLLARS? TWO HUNDRED? THREE HUNDRED?!

That's right! **RUSH YOUR ORDER NOW and receive** *The Hitchhiker's Guide to the Galaxy* and the fluff and the destruct orders and the Don't Panic! button and the sunglasses and the space fleet and no tea **ALL FOR THE INCREDIBLY LOW PRICE OF JUST DA 59.99!**

To save c.o.d., handling charges and Imperial Galactic Government delivery service duties, **PHONE IN YOUR ORDER TODAY!**

# *OPERATORS ARE STANDING BY!*

Call 1-555-55-5-55555-555-5555.
On Ursa Minor Beta, dial
1-5-555-55-55555-555-5555, ext. 5.

# *MAKE THAT CALL TODAY!*

THIS OFFER NOT AVAILABLE IN ANY STORE!*****

***** Except Deluxe-O-Mat, Chain-O-Rama, Qwang's Drive-In Asteroid, Tawdry Merchandise King, House of Remainders, Liquidator's Clearinghouse, Mister Tawdry, Galaxy o' Tawdry Merchandise, Tawdry Merchandise-n-Such, 1-A Tawdry Sales & Service, Ye Olde Tawdry Merchandise Shoppe and MegaMart outlets throughout the Universe.

# ORDER FOR DESTRUCTION

Be it known that on this day the __4__ th day of __October__ in the Year of Our Lord __1982__ that by decree of the Domicile Demolition Department of Cottingshire County, the residence of __Arthur Dent__ at __155 Country Lane__ in __the town of Cottington__ shall herewith be demolished, destroyed and otherwise transformed into a nondescript heap of pulverized rubble; said resident(s) having evacuated said premises within __750__ days of the issuance of this document; this order to be carried out regardless of acknowledgement by said resident(s) of proper notification; said demolition being necessitated by reason of:

(Check one)
- ☐ National emergency.
- ☐ Health hazard.
- ☐ Complex technical matters.
- ☑ It's in the way.

Said property has been seized by Right of Eminent Domain for future use as:

(Check one)
- ☑ Highway right-of-way.
- ☐ Parking facilities.
- ☐ Shopping mall.
- ☐ Wildlife sanctuary.
- ☐ Hunting grounds.
- ☐ New offices for Domicile Demolition Department.
- ☐ Vacant lot.
- ☐ Other (please specify): __________

We the undersigned do hereby authorise the execution of this order through the powers vested in us by the State. God Save the Queen!

Commissioner, Domicile Demolition Department

Vice Commissioner, Domicile Demolition Department

Earle of Cottingshire

DOMICILE DEMOLITION DEPARTMENT

Copy A For Issuance to Resident(s)

## Activision Limited 90-Day Warranty

Activision warrants to the original consumer purchaser of this computer software product that the recording medium on which the software program is recorded will be free from defects in material and workmanship for 90 days from the date of purchase. If the recording medium is found defective within 90 days of original purchase, Activision agrees to replace, free of charge, any product discovered to be defective within such period upon receipt at its Factory service Center of the product, postage paid, with proof of date of purchase, as long as the program is still being manufactured by Activision. In the event that the program is no longer available, Activision retains the right to substitute a similar product of equal or greater value.

This warranty is limited to the recording medium containing the software program originally provided by Activision and is not applicable to normal wear and tear. This warranty shall not be applicable and shall be void if the defect has arisen through abuse, mistreatment, or neglect. Any implied warranties applicable to this product are limited to the 90-day period described above.

To receive a replacement, you should enclose the original product disks accompanied by

- a brief statement describing the defect,
- your name and return address, and
- a photocopy of your dated sales receipt.

Please see the special "RETURNS" information for further instructions.

EXCEPT AS SET FORTH ABOVE, THIS WARRANTY IS IN LIEU OF ALL OTHER WARRANTIES, WHETHER ORAL OR WRITTEN, EXPRESS OR IMPLIED, INCLUDING ANY WARRANTY OF MERCHANTABILITY OR FITNESS OR A PARTICULAR PURPOSE, AND NO OTHER REPRESENTATION OR CLAMS OF ANY KIND SHALL BE BINDING ON OR OBLIGATE ACTIVISION. IN NO EVENT WILL ACTIVISION BE LIABLE FOR SPECIAL, INCIDENTAL, OR CONSEQUENTIAL DAMAGE RESULTING FROM POSSESSION, USE, OR MALFUNCTION OF THIS PRODUCT, INCLUDING DAMAGE TO PROPERTY AND, TO THE EXTENT PERMITTED BY LAW, DAMAGES FOR PERSONAL INJURY, EVEN IF ACTIVISION HAS BEEN ADVISED OF THE POSSIBILITY OF SUCH DAMAGES.

SOME STATES DO NOT ALLOW LIMITATIONS ON HOW LONG AN IMPLIED WARRANTY LASTS AND/OR THE EXCLUSION OR LIMITATION OF INCIDENTAL OR CONSEQUENTIAL DAMAGES, SO THE ABOVE LIMITATIONS AND OR EXCLUSION OR LIMITATION OF LIABILITY MAY NOT APPLY TO YOU. THIS WARRANTY GIVES YOU SPECIFIC LEGAL RIGHTS, AND YOU MAY HAVE OTHER RIGHTS WHICH VARY FROM STATE TO STATE.

## RETURNS

Certified mail is recommended for returns. For best service, please be sure to—

1. Send only the original product disks.
2. Enclose a photocopy of your dated sales receipt.
3. Enclose your name and return address, typed or printed clearly, inside the package.
4. Enclose a brief note describing the problem(s) you have encountered with the software.
5. Write the name of the product and the brand and model name or model number of your computer on the front to the package.

Send to:

Warranty Replacements
Activision
P.O. Box 3048
Menlo Park, CA 94025